TO D. N. S. FOR MANY REASONS

PRENTICE-HALL FOUNDATIONS OF MODERN BIOLOGY SERIES

William D. McElroy and Carl P. Swanson, Editors

NEW VOLUME

Chemical Background for the Biological Sciences, Emil H. White

SECOND EDITIONS

The Cell, Carl P. Swanson

Cell Physiology and Biochemistry, William D. McElroy

Heredity, David M. Bonner and Stanley E. Mills

Adaptation, Bruce Wallace and Adrian M. Srb

Growth and Development, Maurice Sussman

Animal Physiology, Knut Schmidt-Nielsen

Animal Diversity, Earl D. Hanson

Animal Behavior, V. G. Dethier and Eliot Stellar

The Life of the Green Plant, Arthur W. Galston

The Plant Kingdom, Harold C. Bold

Man in Nature, Marston Bates

CARL P. SWANSON   *The Johns Hopkins University*

Englewood Cliffs, New Jersey   **PRENTICE-HALL, INC.**

The Cell

SECOND EDITION

THE CELL, SECOND EDITION, *Carl P. Swanson*

FOUNDATIONS OF MODERN BIOLOGY SERIES

William D. McElroy and Carl P. Swanson, Editors

Design by Walter Behnke

Drawings by Felix Cooper

PRENTICE-HALL INTERNATIONAL, INC., *London*

PRENTICE-HALL OF AUSTRALIA, PTY., LTD., *Sydney*

PRENTICE-HALL OF CANADA, LTD., *Toronto*

PRENTICE-HALL FRANCE, S. A. R. L., *Paris*

PRENTICE-HALL OF INDIA PVT. LTD., *New Delhi*

PRENTICE-HALL OF JAPAN, INC., *Tokyo*

PRENTICE-HALL DE MEXICO, S. A., *Mexico City*

C-112159 (p)   *C-12160 (c)*

Foundations
of Modern Biology
Series

PREFACE TO THE FIRST EDITION

The science of biology today is *not* the same science of fifty, twenty-five, or even ten years ago. Today's accelerated pace of research, aided by new instruments, techniques, and points of view, imparts to biology a rapidly changing character as discoveries pile one on top of the other. All of us are aware, however, that each new and important discovery is not just a mere addition to our knowledge; it also throws our established beliefs into question, and forces us constantly .to reappraise and often to reshape the foundations upon which biology rests. An adequate presentation of the dynamic state of modern biology is, therefore, a formidable task and a challenge worthy of our best teachers.

The authors of this series believe that a new approach to the organization of the subject matter of biology is urgently needed to meet this challenge, an approach that introduces the student to biology as a growing, active science, and that also *permits each teacher of biology to determine the level and structure of his own course.* A single textbook cannot provide such flexibility, and it is the author's strong conviction that these student needs and teacher prerogatives can

vii

best be met by a series of short, inexpensive, well-written, and well-illustrated books so planned as to encompass those areas of study central to an understanding of the content, state, and direction of modern biology. The FOUNDATIONS OF MODERN BIOLOGY SERIES represents the translation of these ideas into print, with each volume being complete in itself yet at the same time serving as an integral part of the series as a whole.

PREFACE TO THE SECOND EDITION

The first edition of the FOUNDATIONS OF MODERN BIOLOGY SERIES represented a marked departure from the traditions of textbook writing. The enthusiastic acceptance of the Series by teachers of biology, here and abroad, has been most heartening, and confirms our belief that there was a long-felt need for flexible teaching units based on current views and concepts. The second edition of all volumes in the Series retains the earlier flexibility, eliminates certain unnecessary overlaps of content, introduces new and relevant information, and provides more meaningful illustrative material.

The Series has also been strengthened by the inclusion of a new volume, *Chemical Background for the Biological Sciences* by Dr. Emil White. The dependence of modern biology on a sound foundation in physics and chemistry is obvious; this volume is designed to provide the necessary background in these areas.

In preparing the second edition of the Series, the authors and editors gratefully acknowledge the many constructive criticisms that have been made by hundreds of teaching biologists. Their interest and aid have made the task of writing more a pleasure than a burden.

Contents

ix

The struggle to know is one of the most exciting dramas of history, and every man who ever tried to learn anything has enacted it for himself to some extent.
— RICHARD R. POWELL

The Cellular Basis of Life

CHAPTER ONE

The biological sciences of today can teach us a profound and meaningful lesson whose validity we can no longer doubt. Their lesson, in brief, is that biology not only recognizes the individuality and uniqueness of every human being and every living organism, but that it, in fact, also supplies compelling evidence for a rational explanation of this individuality in molecular terms. The purpose of this book is to explore the cell, which we now know to be the structural and functional basis of this uniqueness.

We recognize, of course, that the universe around us is not a continuum, a sort of pea-soupy structureless fog. Common experience tells us that it is made up of objects, matter, and other associated phenomena that we can describe or measure. We realize that each of these "things" has a uniqueness that we detect through touch, taste, hearing, smell, or sight, and that each is distinguishable to a greater or lesser degree. With our unaided senses, we have no difficulty in distinguishing the sky and the land from the water, a gas and a solid from a liquid, the living from the nonliving. On a more refined level, we can discriminate degrees of roughness, intensity and shade of color (if we are not color-blind), and an acid taste from one that is salty, sweet, or bitter. But human powers of sensory discrimination are limited. We hear only within a certain range of sound waves, and see only that portion of the light spectrum called the visible region (Fig. 1-1). When we try to go beyond these limits, we can no longer directly comprehend the physical nature of things and must resort to instruments to penetrate areas outside our naturally circumscribed sphere.

Instruments, therefore, act as extended senses. The 200-inch Hale telescope on Mount Palomar reaches across millions of light-years to bring distant galaxies of the macrocosm into view, while light microscopes and electron microscopes reach down into the microcosm to reveal otherwise invisible words. Similarly, photographic plates, more sensitive than our eyes, extend our use of light rays. Ordinarily we can see only a minute portion of the electromagnetic spectrum (Fig. 1-1), but by utilizing photosensitive surfaces we can detect the long infrared rays on one side of the spectrum and the short ultraviolet rays, X-rays, and gamma rays on the other.

Whatever the means we use, the "things" we observe we attempt to define in terms of *units,* and the more refined our knowledge and the more powerful and discriminating our instruments and techniques, the more precise become our definitions of these units, i.e., their limits and basic nature. If we are interested in classification, we find that these units often group themselves into meaningful systems. It would, indeed, be impossible for you to read these pages without understanding letters, the basic units of our language, or the numbers that make up our decimal or metric system.

Fig. 1-1. The electromagnetic spectrum on a log scale, measured in millimeters (mm), microns (μ), and angstrom units (A). 1 μ = 0.001 mm = 10,000 A. The approximate lower limits of resolution of the human eye, the light microscope, and the electron microscope are given.

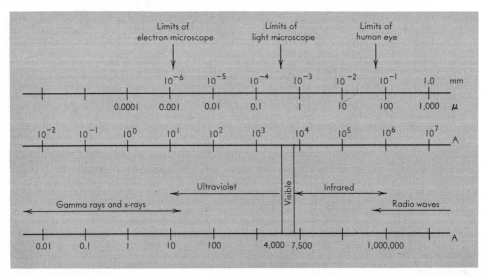

The periodic table of atoms is another example of such a coherent system, and part of its great value lies in enabling us to predict what will happen under specified physical or chemical circumstances. One of the first goals of a science, therefore, whether it be physics, chemistry, or biology, is to determine the uniqueness of the units with which it is concerned, for unless such units are understood and accepted by everyone in a particular field, scientific knowledge in that field cannot progress.

Science makes use of two kinds of units. Those used to describe or to measure time, weight, and distance are arbitrarily defined, but we accept them as standards for the sake of convenience. Thus, millimeters (mm), microns (μ), or Angstroms (A) can be used as convenient measuring units to define limits of the electromagnetic spectrum (Fig. 1-1). Such units as the electron, proton, and neutron, however, have a demonstrated physical reality that can be independently determined by anyone having the proper instruments and required knowledge.

It is the latter type of unit that we will investigate here, for the basic unit of life, the *cell,* is a physical entity. We can break cells up and extract selected parts for study much as the physicist breaks up atoms. We find that these cellular fragments can carry on many of their activities for a time; they may consume oxygen, ferment sugars, and even form new molecules. But these activities individually do not constitute life any more than the behavior of a subatomic particle is equivalent to the behavior of an intact atom. The disrupted cell is no longer capable of continuing life indefinitely, so we conclude that the cell is the elemental unit that can sustain life, even though, as we shall see, the cell, as a unit, is not easy to define.

Compared to the atom and the molecule, the cell, of course, is a unit of far greater size and complexity. It is a microcosm having a definite boundary, within which constant chemical activity goes on. A chemically quiescent cell is dead. The cytologist, therefore, seeks to identify the kinds of cells that exist, to understand their organization and structure in terms of their activities and functions, and to visualize the cell not only as an entity (as it is, for example, in the unicellular bacterium) but also as an integral part of the more elaborate organs and organ systems of multicellular plants and animals.

THE CELL THEORY

The now familiar idea that the cell is the basic unit of life is known as the *cell theory.* You should recognize, however, that the cell theory is more a statement of fact than it is a theory in the conventional sense; i.e., it merely declares that organisms are cellular in structure. Enunciated in 1838–9 by two German scientists, M. J. Schleiden and Theodor Schwann, the former a botanist and the latter a zoologist, the cell theory represented a decisive consolidation and synthesis of biological thought that now ranks with Charles Darwin's *evolution theory* as one of the foundation stones of modern biology. Indeed, we understand life itself only to the extent that we understand the structure and function of cells.

The emergence of a great scientific generalization is generally a slow accumulative process; very few men and their ideas stand alone in the stream of time. The significance of the dates 1838–9 and the names of Schleiden and Schwann, therefore, does not lie in a sudden discovery of cells for the first time. In fact, Robert Hooke, an Englishman, first saw them in 1665 in a piece of cork as he was using his newly invented, primitive microscope (Fig. 1-2). Hooke's observations, however, were not part of a systematic investigation of the structure of living things, and for many years they remained but a casual piece of interesting information unrelated to other biological studies. It was also Hooke who applied the word *cell* to designate the tiny structures he observed in the new world he had discovered.

Schleiden and Schwann were not the first to believe in, or advance, the idea that plants and animals are made of cells and cell products. During the 18th century many workers in Europe described cells and discussed their significance, and by 1800 good microscopes were becoming available, so that more refined observations were possible. There was, in fact, by 1800 a rather general acceptance of the idea that organisms are cellular, but there was much confusion over the definition of cells, their mode of origin, and their significance in development. What Schleiden and Schwann did, however, was to take the loose threads of ideas and observations and weave

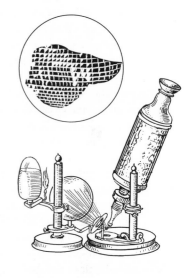

Fig. 1-2. Robert Hooke's drawing of the microscopic structure of cork (in circle), and the microscope with which he observed it. Here, in his own words, is a description of his experiment: "I took a good clear piece of Cork and with a Pen-knife sharpen'd as keen as a razor, I cut a piece of it off, and thereby left the surface of it exceeding smooth, then examining it very diligently with a Microscope, me thought I could perceive it to appear a little porous; but I could not so plainly distinguish them as to be sure that they were pores. . . . I with the same sharp pen-knife cut off from the former smooth surface an exceeding thin piece of it, and placing it on a black object Plate. . . . and casting the light on it with a deep plano-convex Glass, I could exceedingly plainly perceive it to be all perforated and porous, much like a Honeycomb, but that the pores of it were not regular . . . these pores, or cells, were not very deep, but consisted of a great many little Boxes, separated out of one continued long pore by certain Diaphragms . . . Nor is this kind of texture peculiar to Cork only; for upon examination with my Microscope, I have found that the pith of an Elder, or almost any other Tree, the inner pulp or pith of the Cany hollow stalks of several other Vegetables: as of Fennel, Carrets, Daucus, Bur-docks, Teasels, Fearn . . . & c. have much such a kind of Schematisme, as I have lately shewn that of Cork."

them into a convincing and, for that period of biology, a meaningful whole. Even though, as we now recognize, many of their ideas were erroneous, the cell theory was a remarkable act of synthesis and consolidation if not of original discovery. By emphasizing that the cell was both the structural and functional unit of organization and development, they gave coherence to the biological thought of their time and focussed attention on the one structure that had to be understood if biology was to advance beyond its purely descriptive stage.

Some twenty years after the announcements of Schleiden and Schwann, Rudolph Virchow, the great German physician, made another important generalization: *that cells come only from pre-existing cells.* When biologists further recognized that sperm and ova are also cells that unite with each other in the process of fertilization, it gradually became clear that life from one generation to another is an uninterrupted succession of cells. Growth, development, inheritance, evolution, disease, aging, and death are, therefore, but varied aspects of cellular behavior.

Most generalizations have exceptions to them that cast doubt·on their universal validity. This is true as well for the cell theory, but we shall defer a consideration of these exceptions until after we have examined cellular structure in some detail. Let us, however, consider what the cell theory, as presently interpreted, embodies in the way of solid ideas. These are essentially three in number.

In the first place, as we have already mentioned, the cell theory states that life exists only in cells; organisms are therefore made up of cells, and the activity of an organism is dependent on the activities of cells, individually and collectively. We shall find, though, that we may have to modify this idea when we come to discuss the viruses, which lack a conventional cellular organization. Secondly, and as a direct corollary of the first generalization, the cell theory has embodied within it the idea that the continuity of life has a cellular basis, which is another way of stating Virchow's generalization. Now, however, we can be more explicit and enlarge upon this theme, adding that genetic continuity in a very exact sense includes not only the cell as a whole but also some of its smaller components, such as genes and chromosomes. The third idea is that there is a relation between structure and function. This has been called the *principle of complementarity;* it means, briefly, that the biochemical activities of cells occur within, and indeed are determined by, structures organized in a definite way. We shall encounter this idea again in our discussion of cellular components.

André Lwoff, the French microbiologist, has expressed the gist of the cell theory in yet another way: *

When the living world is considered at the cellular level, one discovers unity. *Unity of plan:* each cell possesses a nucleus imbedded in protoplasm. *Unity of*

* A. Lwoff, *Biological Order.* (Cambridge, Mass.: M.I.T. Press, 1962), p. 11, 13.

function: the metabolism is essentially the same in each cell. *Unity of composition:* the main macromolecules of all living beings are composed of the same small molecules. For, in order to build the immense diversity of the living systems, nature has made use of a strictly limited number of buildings blocks. The problem of diversity of structures and functions, the problem of heredity, and the problem of diversification of species have been solved by the elegant use of a small number of building blocks organized into specific macromolecules. . . . Each macromolecule is endowed with a specific function. The machine is built for doing precisely what it does. We may admire it, but we should not lose our heads. If the living system did not perform its task, it would not exist. We have simply to learn how it performs its task.

TOOLS AND TECHNIQUES OF CYTOLOGY

Progress in the life sciences has not followed an even course, for it has been dependent on the development of ever more refined tools and techniques of analysis. This requirement has been especially true for cytology. Some cells may be large enough to see with the unaided eye. But to identify their internal organization we must magnify them greatly, and, more often than not, use dyes that stain selected parts of the cell and not others.

Adequate magnification is as much of a problem for the cytologist as it is for the astronomer; the latter has to overcome great distances, the former very small sizes, in attempting to study in detail the objects they observe. For our purposes, the problem of magnification can best be considered in terms of *resolving power,* which is the property in an optical system of distinguishing between objects lying very close together. In observing a double star, for example, some of you will be able to discern but a single star; others, with better resolving power, will see two separate stars. In a compound microscope, the resolving power of the first magnifying lens is the critical factor. As Fig. 1-3 indicates, the lens nearest the specimen being examined, called the *objective* lens, is the key element of a compound microscope, because the projector lens, the *ocular,* can enlarge only what the objective has resolved.

The unaided human eye has a resolving power of about 0.1 millimeter. Lines closer together than this will be seen as a single line, and objects that have a diameter smaller than this range will be invisible or seen only as blurred images. The human eye, however, has no power of magnification; each of us must calculate sizes mentally, and experience is probably the largest factor in our ability to judge accurately. Microscopes, of course, both resolve and magnify, but their resolving power is limited by the kind of illumination used. Objects that are closer than one-half the wavelength of the illuminating light cannot be clearly distinguished in a light microscope. Thus, even with the most perfectly ground lenses, and with white light having an average wavelength of 5500 Angstroms (A), the objective cannot resolve anything with a diameter less than 2750 A, or 0.275 microns

(μ). Since many parts of cells have lesser dimensions, their presence remained undetected until a means of greater resolution was found.

The *electron microscope* provides this increased resolving power by making use of "illumination" of a different sort. High-speed *electrons* are em-

Fig. 1-3. Schematic representation of the optical systems of the eye, the light microscope, and the electron microscope.

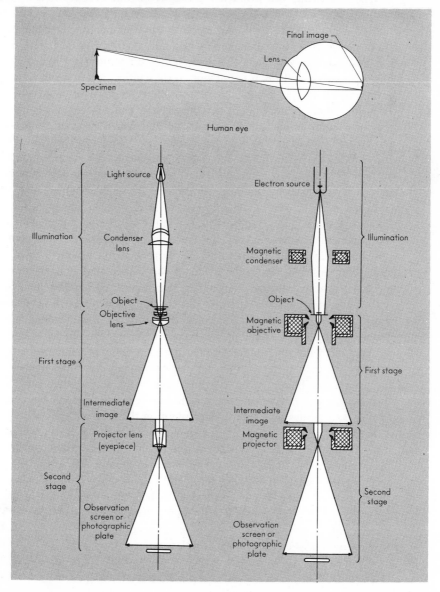

ployed instead of light waves. As these pass through the specimens being viewed, parts of the cell absorb electrons differentially, thus forming an image of the specimen on an electron-sensitive photographic plate or fluorescent screen. The human eye, of course, is not stimulated by electrons, hence the need for plates or screens. The "optical" system is similar to that in the light microscope (Fig. 1-3) except that the "illumination" is focused by magnetic lenses instead of conventional glass lenses.

When electrons are propelled through the microscope by a charge of 50,000 volts, they have a wavelength of about 0.05 A. This is 1/100,000 that of average white light. An electron microscope can thus theoretically resolve objects with a diameter of one-half of 0.05 A, or 0.025 A. This dimension is far less than the diameter of an atom (the hydrogen atom has a diameter of 1.06 A), but due to difficulties in lens construction, the actual resolving power of the best modern instrument is about 10 A. In approximate figures, then, the human eye can resolve down to 100 μ, the light microscope to 0.2 μ, and the electron microscope to 0.001 μ. Or, to put it another way, if the human eye has a resolving power of 1, then that of the light microscope is 500, and that of the electron microscope 10,000. The electron microscope has thus opened up a whole new domain to the cytologist, by making a number of cellular structures visible.

In the study of cells, more than just clear resolution and high magnification are required; the parts of the cell must be clearly distinguished from their immediate surroundings. In the electron microscope, this contrast is possible because some structures are more electron "dense" than others, and photosensitive film is darkened to the degree that it is struck by the electrons passing through a specimen. Such contrast is difficult to achieve with the light microscope because direct light passes through most parts of a cell with equal ease. To overcome this problem, the cytologist uses the proper killing agent (fixative) and stain to bring out the parts he wishes to examine. Literally hundreds of fixing and staining procedures are known; they are the cytologist's recipes, and he continually improves upon them in his search for better ways to study cells. The very active fields of *cytochemistry* and *histochemistry,* which deal respectively with the chemistry of cells and tissues, are greatly dependent on these procedures.

A living cell, however, is always more fascinating than a dead one. To watch cells divide is to witness one of the most dramatic of biological phenomena. The *phase-contrast microscope* permits the cytologist to do this. Various parts of a living cell stand out in sharp contrast when light, slightly out of phase, is passed through; hence, the name of the instrument. Figure 1-4 is a photograph of a living human cancer cell, taken through a phase-contrast microscope. Under the conventional light microscope, such a cell would appear almost structureless.

Another way to study living cells is to "grind" them up and examine their parts. This is done with a special mortar and pestle so as to burst

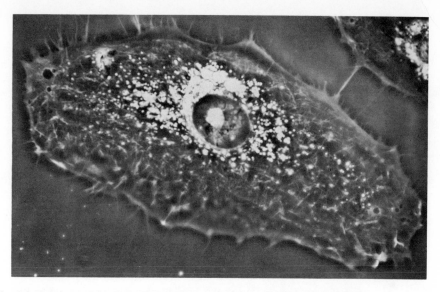

Fig. 1-4. A human cancer cell (HeLa strain) grown in tissue culture and photographed through a phase-contrast microscope. The nucleus with its nucleolus is seen in the center; the white mass is liquid refractile material taken in from the culture medium; the slender rods inside the cell are mitochondria; and the outer fine projections are microfibrils formed by free cells when cultured in test tubes. (Courtesy Dr. George O. Gey.)

the cells and release their contents into a solution. If this solution is then centrifuged at carefully regulated speeds, the heavier portions settle out at lower speeds, the lighter ones at higher speeds. Even the most elusive cellular components can be obtained in substantial amounts and relatively free of other parts. Once separated, each portion can be analyzed for chemical content or tested for chemical activity, since in the test tube some parts continue to function for a while as they did in the intact cells.

Living cells of plants, animals, and humans can also be cultured with ease in much the same way as bacteria or fungi, and subjected to a wide variety of procedures in order to test their response and future behavior. These cells can be probed by microneedles, dissected by the techniques of microsurgery, and injected with solutions through micropipettes. Cells can also be fed substances whose atoms are radioactive; these "tagged" atoms can be followed in the cell and the pathways of reactions unscrambled.

The cytologist, therefore, has a large and varied arsenal of instruments for making the cell give up its secrets. Any one tool or technique, however, is not enough, and he usually employs several methods before an answer can be found to the particular problem being investigated. Such knowledge as we have already garnered from the cell has strengthened our belief that it is the basis of life, while at the same time making us acutely aware of how little we know of its many complexities.

The Structure
of Cells

It is impossible to imagine any biological activity that does
not involve a chemical reaction. Breathing, walking, seeing,
tasting, thinking, or even just existing, requires energy. This
energy, in turn, is derived from chemical reactions that take
place within individual cells. It is also impossible to explain
these activities without a consideration of the structures
related to them: lungs and diaphragm in breathing, muscles
and bones in walking, the lens, retina, and optic nerve of
the eye in seeing. These more obvious structures are made
up of cells, and their molecular arrangement determines their
activity and appearance.

The cell, therefore, can be considered as an organized
chemical factory. It may, of course, be a general-purpose
factory, capable of performing all the services and of manufacturing all the products necessary to continue life; this
must obviously be true in unicellular organisms. Or it may
be a speciality shop, doing only a single kind of job—for
example, nerve cells for communication or muscle cells for
movement. Regardless of its nature, however, a cell, like a
factory, must possess an organization in order to be efficient;

it must contain a controlling center that somehow tells it what to do and when to do it, a source of supplies, a source of energy, and the machinery for making its product or performing its service. It is not surprising, then, that cells, despite their great variety of shapes, sizes, and functions, share many common features. If a cell becomes specialized, we might expect to find a change in organization and, possibly, the appearance of new parts but not at the sacrifice of basic features. For this reason, the biologist considers that *form and function* are inseparable phenomena; to put it another way, organized activity is associated with an organized arrangement of parts.

That biologists recognize the uniqueness of every living organism should alert us that there is no "typical" plant or animal, representative of all plants or animals. We can also extend this concept to the level of cell, for each cell, or cell type, is equally unique. For purposes of discussion, however, we can think of a "typical" cell with the features we wish to examine. This cell is bounded at its outer living limits by a *cell,* or *plasma, membrane,* which separates it from, the environment and through which materials entering or leaving the cell must pass. Our typical cell contains a *nucleus.* This is the center of control of cellular activities; even though the nucleus is necessary for the continued existence of the cell, a cell without a nucleus may continue to function for varying periods of time. The remainder of the cell is the *cytoplasm.* Here are contained the various membrane systems, particulate organelles, and soluble components that, through chemical reactions, control the problems of synthesis and of energy transfer and conversion necessary for the tasks that cells carry out. We still lack many of the pieces of information needed to understand fully the coordinated behavior of this cellular factory, but the major features are reasonably clear.

Much of our understanding has come through the integration of discoveries by biochemists and electron microscopists, the former providing knowledge of the chemical pathways in cells and the latter new concepts in organized cellular morphology. It is now possible to speak with some assurance about the *fine structure* of the cell in molecular terms, and to view the various structures in the light of their function.

Here it should be mentioned that the use of the electron microscope in revealing the fine structure of cells was enhanced by the parallel development of techniques for the cutting of ultrathin slices of cells. An ordinary microtome, used in connection with light microscopy, can cut sections about 4 to 5 microns thick. Thus, a cell 30 μ in diameter could be sliced into 6 or 7 pieces; these, however, would be too thick for use in electron microscopy, since the electron beam would be largely absorbed by this amount of material and would therefore reveal but little of cellular morphology. By new sectioning techniques we can now cut slices between 100 to 500 A (1/100 to 1/20 of a micron) in thickness. A comparable cell could thus yield about 600 cross-sections. This refinement means of course that the electron microscope, because of its tremendous powers of resolution, can only reveal very minute portions of a cell at any given time; in a sense, breadth of vision is sacrificed for intimate details. A comparison of various photographs in this book taken through the light and electron microscopes will convey something of the great steps forward that have been achieved in resolution during the past 20 years.

In order to preserve cells for sectioning, new techniques of fixation and embedding also had to be developed. The most successful fixatives are osmium tetroxide, potassium permanganate, and formaldehyde, and thin sectioning requires that the material be embedded in plastic resins instead of the usual paraffin.

THE CELL SURFACE

Before the electron microscope came into general use, it was assumed that all cells had an outer limiting membrane that separated each one from the environment and thereby preserved the identity of the cell as a basic unit of organization. Studies with the electron microscope have confirmed the universal existence of this plasma membrane and have shown that it is invisible in the light microscope because it is about 100 A, or 0.01 μ, thick, and thus below the limits of ordinary resolution.

The double nature and molecular make-up of the plasma membrane are depicted in Fig. 2-1. The idea that the membrane has a lipoprotein (fat plus protein) composition preceded studies with the electron microscope, and arose out of work done primarily on the permeability and surface tension of various kinds of cells. The protein constituent of the membrane gives the cell wettability and flexibility. Since protein molecules, which are long and complex, can fold or unfold, the membrane can expand or contract, thus providing through molecular spacing a possible means of control over which molecules can enter the cell from the outside environment, or pass to the environment from inside the cell. Such a membrane is said

Fig. 2-1. Upper, the plasma membrances of adjacent cells, showing their layered nature. (Courtesy Dr. J. D. Robertson.) Below, an interpretation of the plasma membrane in molecular terms. The open circles on outer and inner sides are protein molecules, while the tadpole-shaped structures represent a double sandwich of lipid (fat) molecules. The whole structure is referred to as a "unit membrane."

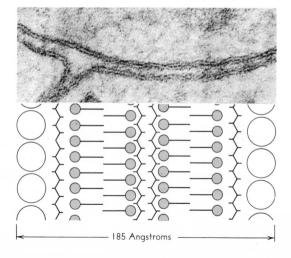

185 Angstroms

to be *selectively permeable,* with the degree of permeability related to the state of the membrane at any given time. Such a membrane would also permit growth and movement, either for the cell as a whole or for localized regions, as is the case in an amoeba when it moves along the surface of a glass dish. The mechanics of membrane contraction, expansion, or growth are not, however, fully understood.

The lipid portion of the membrane is suggested by the fact that fat solvents readily penetrate cells from the surrounding environment, but the structural or functional role of the lipids is not well understood.

Even so, the basic nature of the membrane, as depicted in Fig. 2-1, seems characteristic of all cell membranes, and it may well be that this kind of molecular structure provides a surface on which specific cellular reactions can take place with relative ease. We shall discuss this problem more fully when we consider a part of the cell called the mitochondrial membrane. But for now we can note this: It is known that the outer membrane of a bacterial cell possesses, either as an integral part or in close association, a group of enzymes called *permeases* that govern, in part, the permeability of the cell to various molecules.

Other problems of membrane permeability are discussed in another volume of this series,* but it is of interest to us here that free cells, such as those in tissue culture, can engulf materials from the liquid environment by one or both of two additional processes, *pinocytosis* and *phagocytosis.* The former name is derived from the Greek words for "drink" and "cell," and the process is literally a drinking phenomenon. The flexible plasma membrane forms a channel to get liquids into the cell, and then pinches off pockets that are incorporated into the cytoplasm to be digested (Fig. 2-2). By this device, large molecules incapable of passing through the membrane can be taken up by cells. In *phagocytosis* (from the Greek *phagein,* to eat), arms of cytoplasm engulf solid material such as bacteria, draw these materials into the cytoplasm where the membranes break down and enzymes digest the particles (Fig. 2-3).

We can, therefore, consider the plasma membrane a portion of the living cell. This point of view is reinforced by the intimate connections of the plasma membrane with other internal membrane systems (Fig. 2-4), its capability of limited repair if torn or punctured by a needle, and its activity in a cell exhibiting pinocytosis, phagocytosis, or mobility. We must recognize, however, that the membrane is elastic, changeable, and pliable in some cells, quite rigid and unyielding in others; thin in a cell such as that depicted in Fig. 1-4, thick in some marine invertebrate eggs; smooth in an ameba, ciliated in Paramecium. We must recognize further that cell surfaces differ in physiological response. Red blood cells of the A, B, and O types are indistinguishable morphologically, but readily separable on the

* W. D. McElroy, *Cell Physiology and Biochemistry,* 2nd ed. (Englewood Cliffs, N. J.: Prentice-Hall, 1964).

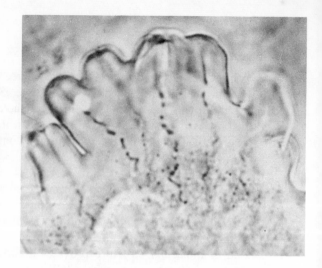

Fig. 2-2. Photograph of the edge of a living ameba showing the pinocytotic channels (the dark lines converging toward the center of the cell). Liquids flow into the cell through these channels, to be pinched off as membrane-enclosed droplets; these eventually dissolve in the interior of the cell. (Courtesy Dr. David Prescott.)

Fig. 2-3. The phagocytotic process, with arms of cytoplasm engulfing a solid particle from the outer environment. These particles, after being drawn into the cell, can be attacked and digested by the cell enzymes.

Fig. 2-4. A schematic representation of the possible interrelations of the various external and internal membrane systems of the cell. The diagram suggests that all membranes have a common structure and a common origin. (Courtesy Dr. J. D. Robertson.)

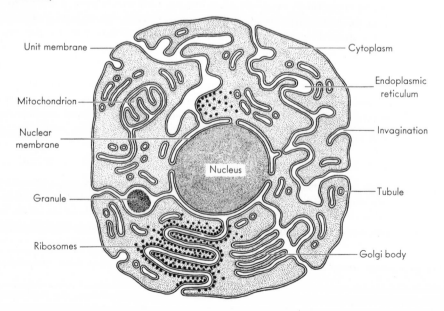

basis of their clumping reaction when exposed to blood sera of different kinds. Cells from the same tissue also exhibit the ability to "recognize" one another when in liquid suspension. For example, if heart and retinal cells from a chick embryo are dissociated to form a mixed single-cell suspension, heart cells seek out and aggregate with heart cells, retinal cells with retinal cells. Cell membranes, therefore, possess discrete properties such as movement and mutual adhesiveness. Some of these properties may be conferred upon the plasma membrane by associated molecules—e.g., the glyco- or mucoproteins of red blood cells—but the membrane itself may possess distinct arrangements of parts that determine its ultimate functional character. The similarity of appearance of membranes demonstrated by electron microscopy may consequently be deceptive and may obscure a molecular diversity that can only be revealed by other experimental techniques.

In concluding our discussion of the plasma membrane, we should not leave the impression that this structure is a simple envelope, comparable to a thin plastic bag surrounding the cell contents. Two examples will show how its contours may be modified in certain specialized cells. Figure 2-5 is of a columnar epithelial cell in the lining of the small intestine of the mouse; such a cell is active in the absorption of digested food. The plasma membrane here is greatly convoluted, and contains regions that show intimate connections—*desmosomes*—with adjacent cells, while the upper surface of the cell forms a "brush border" in which the many projections—*microvilli*—provide a tremendous absorption area. Each such cell would have upwards of 3000 individual microvilli, while a square millimeter of the intestine would have as many as 200,000,000.

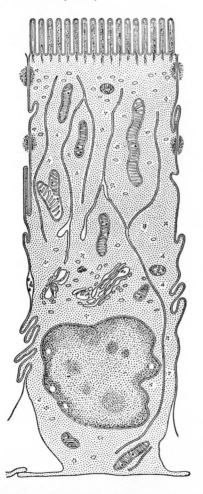

Fig. 2-5. Schematic drawing of a columnar epithelial cell from the small intestine of a mouse, showing how the plasma membrane can be folded along its sides, and greatly convoluted (top) to form the microvilli that are active in absorption (see Fig. 2-10 for details). (From H. Zetterqvist, Thesis, U. of Stockholm, 1956.)

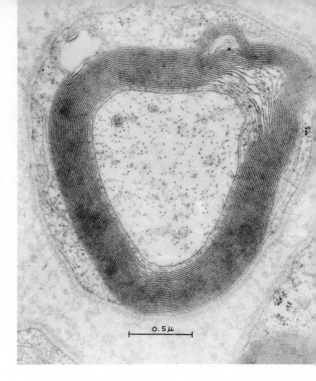

Fig. 2-6. Electron micrograph cross section through a nerve fiber, with the membranes of the Schwann cell wrapped around the central axon. The cytoplasm of the Schwann cell can be seen outside of the membranes and between the disrupted layers of membranes at the upper right. The basement membrane (see Chap. 3) of extra-cellular materials lies on the extreme outside, surrounding the entire structure. (Courtesy Dr. L. G. Elfvin.)

In a gross way, the lining of an intestine is comparable to the absorptive surface of a bath towel.

The relation between a nerve cell and its associated *Schwann,* or *satellite, cells* presents another situation where the plasma membrane forms an elaborate structural system. Figure 2-6 depicts a nerve fiber, or axon—the extended process of a nerve—with the associated Schwann cell wrapped around the axon. The development of the spiral proceeds as in Fig. 2-7. The cytoplasm of the Schwann cell is largely squeezed to the out-

Fig. 2-7. Schematic representation of the progressive envelopment of an axon by the membranes of the Schwann cell, as described by Dr. Betty G. Geren. Such an axon is said to be myelinated.

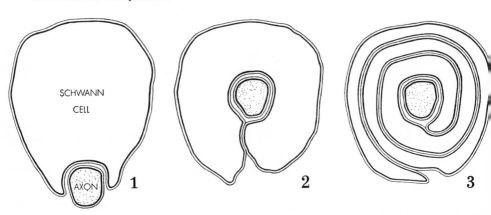

side in this process, leaving the axon surrounded by a multilayered membrane system that probably protects the nerve, and assists in the transmission of nerve impulses and in the nutrition of the long and tenuous axon.

THE ENDOPLASMIC RETICULUM

If a living cell has its plasma membrane ruptured, the cytoplasm oozes out as a slightly viscous liquid. This suggests that there is little structural organization of cytoplasmic materials, but this view of the cytoplasm has been drastically altered by the electron microscopists. In cells of almost every kind (the mammalian red blood cell is an exception), there exists an elaborate system of membranes that, we now recognize, is an important part of the cell for the manufacture of cellular products. This is the *endoplasmic reticulum* (ER), or *ergastoplasm* (Fig. 2-8), a membrane-limited cisternal (sac-like) system extending, in various degrees, from the *nuclear membrane* on the inside to the plasma membrane on the outside of the cell. The nuclear membrane can be considered a part of the ER, or to turn the picture around, the ER is an extension of the outer membrane of the nucleus into the cytoplasm. This point of view is suggested by the relations depicted in Fig. 2-4 where the outer layer of the nuclear membrane is continuous with the cytoplasmic membrane system and the plasma membrane.

The ER is of a variable morphology, and although each kind of cell has a characteristic ER, it must be considered a labile cytoplasmic system that can probably alter its nature rapidly. As Fig. 2-8 shows, the ER can be loosely organized or its membranes can be tightly packed in the cytoplasm. Furthermore, the membranes can be either rough or smooth.

The rough, or *granular,* ER is found in great abundance in those cells engaged in protein synthesis. This chemical capacity resides in electron-dense particles that are rich in ribose nucleic acid (RNA). Since *ribosomes* may, however, lie free in the cytoplasm, their association with the ER is not necessary. In fact, bacteria, which seem to possess little or no ER, are nevertheless rich in ribosomal particles. The association of ribosomes with membranes, on the other hand, does provide the intact cell with a means of compartmentalizing specific chemical reactions. Note in this connection, that ribosomes must differ in their protein-forming capacity even though all have a similar appearance, since each cell must be capable of producing the numerous protein molecules it needs for structural or functional purposes. Further, note that the membranes also provide a tremendous increase in surface area within the cell. If we accept the point of view that enzymes

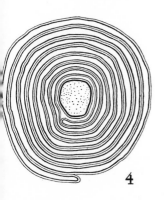
4

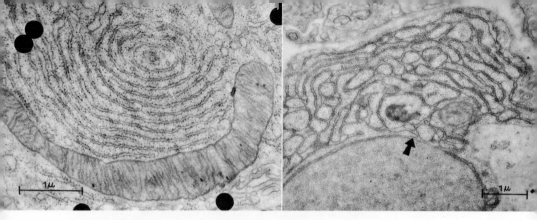

Fig. 2-8. The endoplasmic reticulum in parotid (salivary gland) acinous cells of the mouse. Left, the ER above the mitochondrion is of the rough, or granular, variety, containing ribosomes, and is much more highly organized than in the area immediately below; many of the membranes end blindly in the cytoplasm. Right, the mass of rough ER membranes is a continuously branching and interconnected system, which is also connected with the outer portion of the nuclear membrane (arrow). (Courtesy Dr. H. F. Parks.)

are part of membrane systems, then the cell can possess local patterns of synthesis.

This concept is reinforced by the activity of the smooth, or *agranular,* ER, which lacks the ribosomes (Fig. 2-9). There is probably no sharp morphological discontinuity between the smooth and rough kinds of ER, but the former is particularly prevalent in those cells engaged in the synthesis of fatty substances, i.e., lipids as in the cells of sebaceous glands, or steroid hormones in certain endocrine glands. The enzymes necessary for these syntheses appear to be a part of the membrane itself since they cannot be separated physically from the membrane fragments.

Fig. 2-9. Electron micrograph of a portion of a cell from the testis of an opossum, showing the smooth, or agranular, form of endoplasmic reticulum. (Courtesy Dr. D. Fawcett.)

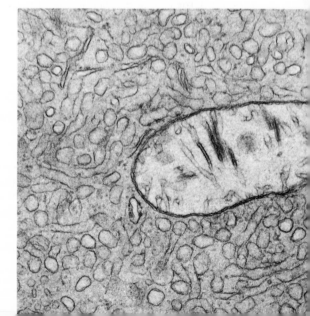

The ER, therefore, is a kind of cytoskeleton providing surfaces for chemical reactions, pathways for the transport of materials, and collection depots for synthesized materials. We also find the smooth ER, in particular, in those cells that must maintain a particular shape; in these the ER is a structural component as well. This role is particularly evident in the light-receptor cells in the retina of a number of different organisms, where the ER is built into an elaborate and compact latticework of membranes (Fig. 2-10). These cells receive light and transmit this information via the membranes to the nervous system of the organism, but the details of this process remain to be clarified.

THE GOLGI COMPLEX

Comparable to the smooth ER, but discontinuous, smaller, and more compact in nature, the *Golgi complex,* so named after its discoverer, is another characteristic system of cytoplasmic membranes. The term, *dictysome,* is also used to describe this structure. Whether there is a direct morphological relation between the ER and the Golgi complex is still debatable; the Golgi complex, however, was early recognized by its affinity for osmium or silver-containing stains. Figure 2-11 reveals the details made visible through electron microscopy.

The function of the Golgi complex

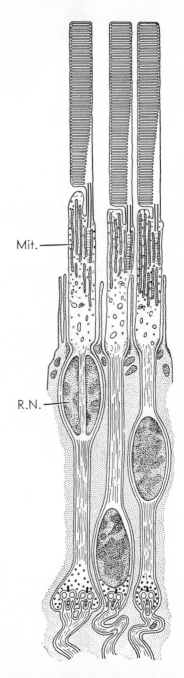

Fig. 2-10. Schematic representation of a rod (light-receptor) cell in the retina of the guinea pig. The smooth ER at the top of the cell is folded and refolded to provide many layers of membranes, each of which contains light-sensitive pigments on its surface. The mitochondria are concentrated just below the light-sensitive area; the rod nucleus is also identified. At the base, each cell has an intimate connection with a nerve fiber. (Dr. F. S. Sjöstrand, International Review of Cytology, Vol. 5, 1956; with permission, Academic Press.)

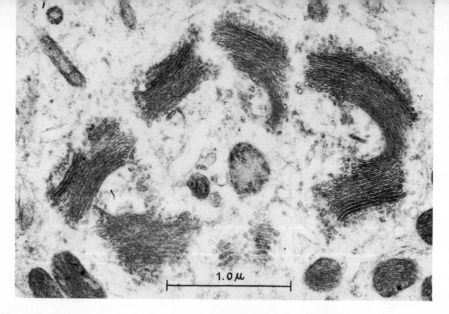

Fig. 2-11. Electron micrograph of Golgi complexes as they occur in the spermatid (immature sperm cell) of a snail. (Courtesy Dr. A. H. Dalton.)

is still somewhat in doubt but since its membranes have little RNA it is not concerned with protein synthesis. Rather, the general consensus today is that it is somehow involved in the storage and possible modification of lipid substances, a point of view supported by observations that the appearance of the Golgi complex in animal cells can be modified greatly by changes in fat diet.

CYTOPLASMIC PARTICLES

The cytoplasmic membrane systems of the cell are not concerned solely with the production of cellular products, or simply utilized for structural purposes. The production of a product, the formation of a structure, or the performance of a service (e.g., transmission of nerve impulses) also requires energy and/or raw materials, and these must be handled efficiently by some part of the cell for the benefit of the whole cell. The raw materials, of course, pass into the cell through the plasma membrane from the outside environment. For our purposes here, we need only assume that these materials are in ready supply, and that, together with a source of energy, the cell can transform them into more of its own unique substance through the processes of metabolism. The larger particulate structures—*plastids* and *mitochondria*—are mainly concerned with the energy problem of the cell; these are also of a membranous nature.

The sun is the ultimate source of all energy needed in the maintenance and continuation of life. This energy arrives at the surface of the earth in the form of heat and light. Since the cell can function only within a limited range of temperature, heat energy cannot be used to any major extent, but light energy can. The cell, through long ages of change, has evolved the machinery to do this job.

The sequence of the trapping of light energy, its conversion into chemical energy, and its storage in molecules derived from CO_2 and water, is known as *photosynthesis*. This process is described elsewhere in this series; * here we need only note that photosynthesis is initiated by the capture of light energy through absorption in the green pigment *chlorophyll*. The *chloroplast* is the cytoplasmic particle in which this takes place.

Electron microscopy reveals that the chloroplast is a structure of considerable complexity (Fig. 2-12). It is bound by a membrane, and is organized internally into a series of lamellar areas (*grana*) and nonlamellar areas (*stroma*). The grana can be visualized as pieces of many-layered plywood lying in a less well-organized stroma. Within the grana, the chlorophyll molecules are precisely oriented in a monolayer sandwiched in

* W. D. McElroy, *Cell Physiology and Biochemistry*, 2nd. ed.; A. W. Galston, *The Life of the Green Plant*, 2nd ed. (Englewood Cliffs, N. J.: Prentice-Hall, 1964).

Fig. 2-12. Electron micrographs of a chloroplast from a spinach leaf, showing the grana (g), intergrana spaces (ig), stroma (s), membrane surrounding a vacuole (t), and the cell wall (cw). Right, a more highly magnified portion showing the distinct lamellar arrangement in the grana. (Courtesy G. Schidlofsky.)

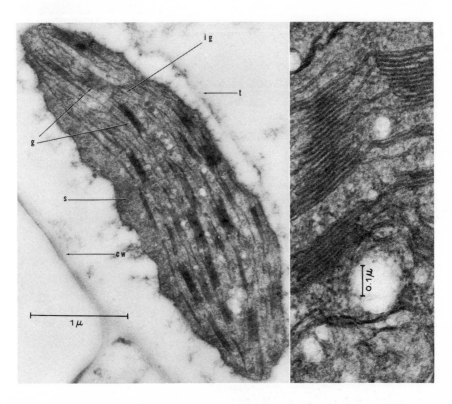

between layers of proteins and intimately associated with lipids and carotenoids (Fig. 2-13), an arrangement that makes for efficiency not only in the trapping of light energy but for its conduction and utilization in photosynthesis. The stroma is best thought of as the aqueous part of the chloroplast, containing dissolved salts and enzymes, but as Calvin's diagram suggests, enzymes are also part of the lamellar structure of the grana.

Any disturbance induced in the lamellar structure of a granum leads to a reduction in its efficiency. For example, when the unicellular alga, Euglena, is grown in the dark for long periods it loses its green color; when this happens the chloroplasts fragment and the lamellae disappear. When this organism gets light again, the formation of lamellae and chlorophyll proceeds simultaneously. Within 4 hours, thin lamellae can be seen forming; by 72 hours, the fully-formed chloroplast is evident.

Fig. 2-13. Schematic representation of the layered arrangement of lamellae in the grana (above), and the possible arrangement of molecules in a lamella (below). The enzymes involved in photosynthesis are part of the protein layers, and the carotenoid and phospholipid molecules assist in the transfer of energy captured by the chlorophyll. (After A. J. Hodge and M. Calvin.)

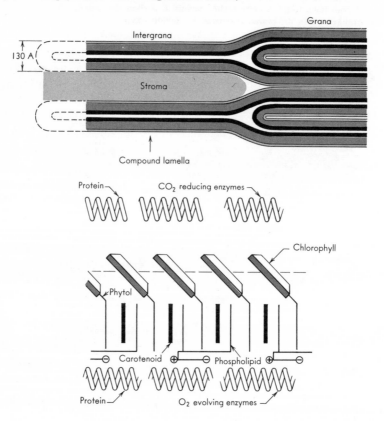

From this kind of information we can conclude that an ordered lamellar structure is necessary for photosynthesis to occur; structure and function are interrelated. Biologists have long hoped that they could induce solutions of chlorophyll to photosynthesize in a test tube, and thus provide a method for the efficient production of sugars. It seems likely, though, that they will have to find someway to arrange the molecules in an ordered sequence before they can accomplish this.

Chloroplasts may assume many forms, and vary widely in number per cell, in different plants. In some algae, such as the filamentous Spirogyra, only a single chloroplast is present in each cell; when the cell divides, it divides at the same time. In contrast, a cell in the spongy part of a grass leaf may have 30 to 50 chloroplasts; their division, which occurs in the immature, or proplastid, state, is not correlated with cell division in any exact way. The grana may be missing in some chloroplasts, as in some brown algae, to be replaced by long membranes running the length of the chloroplast, but these presumably function in the same manner as the grana. The blue-green algae, on the other hand, lack definite chloroplasts; instead they possess loosely arranged membranes in the cytoplasm on which the photosynthetic pigments are layered. Only in bacterial cells do we find a photosynthetic capacity associated with nonmembranous structure. Here the vacuolar-like *chromatophores* are the photosynthetic units, but we know little about the molecular arrangement of the light-absorbing pigments. However, bacteria kept in the dark lose their chromatophores and are no longer photosynthetic; the chromatophore thus behaves as the chloroplast of Euglena, and is its functional, but not structural, equivalent.

All *plastids* do not contain chlorophyll and function photosynthetically. Some, as in the potato tuber, are for starch storage; others may contain oil or protein. These lack the lamellar construction of the chloroplast. However, they are derived from a common type of plastid in the cell and what each becomes depends upon the kind of cell in which it is found at maturity.

Most students who have a nodding acquaintance with biology think of photosynthesis only as the utilization of light energy to reduce CO_2 into simple sugar molecules, with the necessary hydrogen atoms being derived from water. But there is more to it than that. We now know that the light energy trapped by chlorophyll can also be funneled, through a series of enzymatically controlled reactions, into an energy-rich compound called *adenosine triphosphate,* or *ATP.** The chloroplast is, therefore, a dual energy-converter, since the energy of sugars and ATP can be utilized by the cell in a variety of ways.

Another type of energy converter is the *mitochondrion* (Fig. 2-14) found in virtually every type of cell (bacteria, blue-green algae, and the mammalian

---

* Discussed more fully in W. D. McElroy, *Cell Physiology and Biochemistry,* 2nd ed. (Englewood Cliffs, N. J.: Prentice-Hall, 1964).

Fig. 2-14. Highly magnified electron micrograph of a mitochondrion in a mouse pancreatic cell. The outer boundary of the mitochondrion is a double structure, with the inner layer being continuous with the inner cross membranes (cristae). (Courtesy Dr. B. L. Munger.)

red blood cells are exceptions). In living cells they are in constant motion. They range in size from 0.2 to about 5.0 μ, and their shape may be rod-like or spherical, although shape, size, and internal structure all tend to be characteristic of a given cell type or organism. A rat liver cell of about 25 μ diameter may contain as many as 1000 mitochondria. Indeed, wherever cellular activity is high they tend to cluster: at the junction where nerve cells meet and transmit impulses across membranes; around actively beating sperm tails; just under the brush border of intestinal epithelial cells when absorption is going on; and at those regions of muscle cells that are particularly concerned with contraction. This kind of mitochondrial aggregation is not accidental, for as we now realize, these organelles have an important role in energy transmission.

Let us first consider their structure, which has been beautifully revealed by the high resolution of the electron microscope. A double lipoprotein membrane, similar apparently to the plasma and nuclear membranes, surrounds each individual mitochondrion. The inner membrane can be variously folded into *cristae* to provide a great interior surface area. This is depicted diagrammatically in Figure 2-15. The outer membrane is quite elastic, to judge from the mitochondrion's ability to swell or contract with relative ease. The size of substances entering the mitochondrion depends on the degree of stretching of the membrane, and there is further evidence to suggest that the activity of the mitochondrion also varies as it swells or contracts. The inside of the mitochondrion is the liquid phase, or *matrix,* as contrasted with the membrane phase; both phases, as we shall see, have their particular roles to play in cellular metabolism, and both can be separated and tested in mitochondria that have been isolated from burst cells through differential centrifugation.

The mitochondria are the respiratory centers of the cell. The carbohydrates, proteins, and fats to be used as metabolic fuel are broken down by enzymes outside of the mitochondrion into their respective smaller fragments: pyruvic, amino, and fatty acids. These can pass through the mitochondrial membrane into the matrix where enzymatic reactions "chip" off carbon atoms, one at a time from pyruvic and amino acids, two at a time from fatty acids. Since oxygen is involved in the process, this is known as *oxidation,* and the end products are CO_2, water, and chemical energy. The energy, however, is not liberated as heat, but is passed along in a repackaged chemical form and ultimately into ATP. As in the chloroplast, the mitochondrion forms ATP as part of an energy-trapping process, and these concentrated packets of energy can then be moved to the parts of the cell where needed. The breakdown of these metabolic fuels occurs in the liquid interior of the mitochondrion where many enzymes exist in soluble form. ATP production, however, is a primary function of the

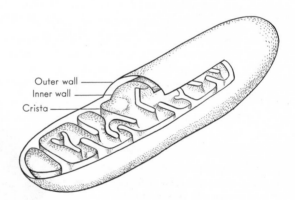

Outer wall
Inner wall
Crista

Fig. 2-15. Schematic drawing of a typical mitochondrion. (Courtesy Dr. A. H. Lehninger.)

mitochondrial membrane, and evidence shows that part of the fabric of the inner membrane consists of assemblies of enzymes that transfer electrons from one site to another until they finally are incorporated into ATP. This process is known as *oxidative phosphorylation.*

The experimental separation of the two systems of enzymes was accomplished by rupturing the mitochondrion. Approximately 70 mitochondrial enzymes are known; the oxidative enzymes appeared in solution, but it was difficult to separate the phosphorylating enzymes from the membrane. A possible arrangement of this assembly of enzymes is shown in Fig. 2-16; it is thought that each mitochondrion possesses up to 20,000 of these assemblies. If this is a correct assessment of the situation, the membrane serves a dual purpose being a structural and functional mosaic. Other evidence, however, visualizes the enzyme assemblies as attached to the membrane in the manner of ribosomes on the ER. The situation, therefore, remains to be fully clarified.

We can see, therefore, that the capture, conversion, and transfer of energy are intimately tied in with cellular organization. The chloroplast captures solar energy while the mitochondrion transforms the energy bound up in molecular fuels; both repackage energy in the form of sugars or ATP, which are then used by the cell as needed.

Other mitochondrial-like structures are also found in the cytoplasm of most cells. These are the *lysosomes*. They are distinguishable from the mitochondria by their lack of internal cristae and by their characteristic enzyme content. The lysosomes may be thought of as intracellular digestive systems; the contained enzymes are mainly hydrolases, and their principal function is the destruction of large molecules, even membrane fragments, by the addition of water. The breakdown products presumably diffuse out of the lysosomes and into the mitochondria, where they are further broken down in the process of respiration.

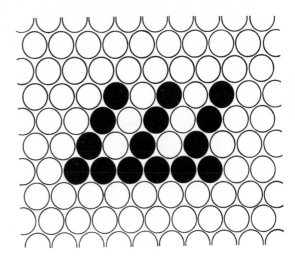

Fig. 2-16. Schematic drawing of a suggested arrangement of the phosphorylating enzymes (shown by black circles) in an "assembly line," and embedded in the protein wall (shown by open circles). (Courtesy Dr. A. H. Lehninger.)

OTHER CELLULAR COMPONENTS

Two other cellular structures need mention apart from the nucleus, which we shall consider shortly. One is the *vacuole,* the other the *centrosome.*

Vacuoles, or fluid-filled membrane-enclosed spaces within the cytoplasm, are more prominent in plant than in animal cells. They probably arise by expansion of the open spaces (cisternae) in the ER; this is suggested not only by developmental studies but also by the single-layer form of the vacuolar membrane, or *tonoplast,* which is like that of the membranes of the ER. In most plant cells except those undergoing cell division, the vacuole occupies the major portion of the cell volume (Fig. 2-17). Located centrally, as a rule, the vacuole forces the cytoplasm to the outside of the cell, where a ready exchange of gases can occur. This would be of obvious advantage to a cell engaged in photosynthesis since CO_2 and O_2 would not have to pass through a thick mass of cytoplasm.

The vacuoles serve also to maintain the proper internal pressure in cells. Sugars, salts, and other dissolved materials in the vacuoles make the vacuolar fluid more hypertonic than the outer environment; water, consequently, will move into the cell by osmosis and maintain the turgidity of the cell. In protozoa, a more complex vacuole which is capable of contraction probably acts to eject excess water or waste fluids from the cell to the outside. Food vacuoles, also found in protozoa, are membrane-enclosed particles that will be digested by enzymes secreted into it from the cytoplasm.

Another function performed by plant vacuoles is that of providing a dumping ground for unwanted materials. Many kinds of crystalline materials are found in them, particularly crystals of calcium oxalate, and it may well be that this provides a means of getting rid of noxious materials the cell no longer needs or can use.

The centrosome, with its centriole, is a structure more characteristic of animal than of plant cells. Lying just outside the nuclear membrane, it functions in cell division. Its role has long been known. Its structure, however, remained a mystery until recently when it was demonstrated through electron microscopy that, like most cellular organelles, it possesses a high degree of inter-

Fig. 2-17. Three examples of plant cells, illustrating the manner by which the formation of a vacuole pushes the cytoplasm to the outside, thus increasing the exchange of materials between the cytoplasm and the exterior of the cell. (A) Cells from the one-cell-thick skin in an onion bulb; (B) Cell from the stamen hair of the spiderwort, Tradescantia; **(C) Typical cell of a leaf, showing the plastids, nucleus, and cytoplasm forced to the outside. Strands of cytoplasm may often cross through the vacuole, as shown in (B).**

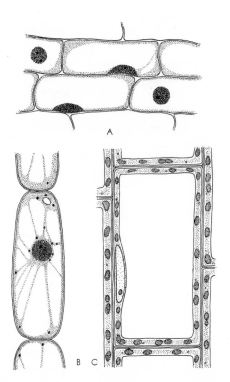

A

B C

nal organization. About 3000 to 5000 A long and 1500 A in diameter, the centriole is a cylindrical structure containing nine double tubules arranged in a circle, each tubule being about 200 A in diameter. Such a structure is, in cross-section, reminiscent of the organization found in sperm tails, *cilia,* and *flagella* (Fig. 2-18), except that the central pair of tubules is absent in the centriole.

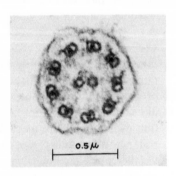

0.5 μ

Fig. 2-18. Electron micrograph cross-section of the sperm tail in the mouse, showing the nine double tubules forming an outer ring, and a double tubule in the center. The structure of the centriole would be similar with the exception that the central pair of tubules would be missing. (Courtesy Dr. T. Nagano.)

THE NUCLEUS

The most prominent feature of a cell, when viewed under the microscope, is the nucleus (Fig. 1-4). This is the controlling center of the cell, for in it are found the chromosomes and genes that determine the character of each individual cell.

The significance of the nucleus may be judged from two types of experiments. In an ameba, for example, it is possible to remove the nucleus by means of surgery or with a microneedle or pipette. The cytoplasm is not damaged by such surgery, and the cell can metabolize for several days or even weeks since the requisite cytoplasmic enzymes and organelles are still functioning. The cell eventually runs down, however, and is unable to rejuvenate itself unless another nucleus is put back into the cytoplasm. We can, therefore, view an enucleated cell as a cell without a future, and the nucleus as a necessary organelle providing information or parts to the cytoplasm to keep it functioning properly for an indefinite period.

The nucleus is also the source of information that governs the morphology of cells. We might have assumed this from the distinctive shapes of many unicellular organisms, but experiments done by the German biologist Max Hämmerling, on *Acetabularia,* a single-celled green alga of warm marine waters, demonstrate this beautifully. Two species of *Acetabularia* differ in the shape of their caps (Fig. 2-19). If a cap is cut off, it will reform again; it is also possible to graft a piece of the stalk of one species onto the decapitated, nucleus-containing *rhizoid* of the other species. When the cap forms again it is characteristic of the species that contributed the nucleus and not that of the species that contributed the stalk plus its contained cytoplasm. When two rhizoids, both containing nuclei, are grafted together the cap that forms is intermediate in character, reflecting the influence of both nuclei. The nucleus, therefore, causes a cell to do as it dictates.

In appearance, the nucleus is generally a rounded body, although it may also be flattened into a lens shape or even be lobed. It is bounded on its outside by a double-layered *nuclear* membrane, the outside member of which, as Fig. 2-4 suggests, is continuous with the membranes of the endoplasmic reticulum. Figure 2-20 shows this more clearly. The structure and arrangement of the membranes, indeed, suggest that the nucleus is enveloped by a deep fold of the outer plasma membrane, although it should be recognized that the thin sectioning required in electron microscopy would not permit the ready tracing of the membranes throughout the entire cell.

The outer membrane of the nucleus does possess a peculiarity, that tends to set it apart from other membrane systems: It has a series of pores, which vary with the type of cell. These are visible in Fig. 2-20. Whether such pores permit the passage of large molecules in and out of the cell is a matter of current controversy.

When the nucleus is stained with basic dyes such as crystal violet or haemotoxylin, the central portion shows up as a network of fine threads in

Fig. 2-19. Influence of the nucleus on development in Acetabularia. Stalk segments of A. mediterranea grafted onto nucleus-containing rhizoids of A. crendulata, and vice versa, produce caps characteristic of the species contributing the nucleus. When two nucleus-containing rhizoids are grafted together, the cap consists of loose rays, as in A. crenulata, but their points are more rounded, as in A. mediterranea.

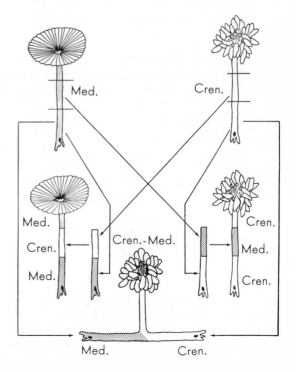

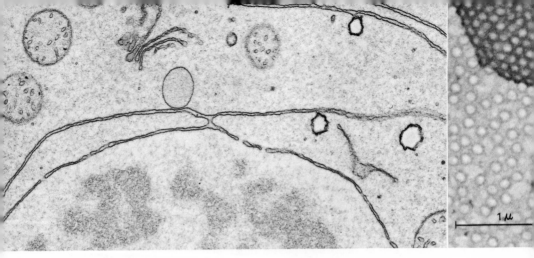

Fig. 2-20. Electron micrographs of nuclear membranes. Left, portion of a plant cell with the nucleus and shadowy chromosomes at the bottom; the double nature of the nuclear membrane, the pores, and the connection of the outer portion of the nuclear membrane with the endoplasmic reticulum can be seen. (Courtesy Dr. G. Whaley.) Right, a face-on view of the nuclear membrane from a frog's egg, showing the regular arrangement of the nuclear pores; the darker portion is an overlying membrane fragment. (Courtesy Dr. R. W. Merriam.)

which coarser lumps of heavier materials stand out (Fig. 2-21). This is the *chromatin,* or the chromosomes of the cell in an extended and diffuse state, which permits maximum surface contact with the surrounding *nuclear sap.* The diffuse state of the chromatin is believed necessary since the nondividing cell is really in its most active metabolic condition.

Also present in the nucleus are dense, rounded bodies, the *nucleoli* (sing., *nucleolus*) (Fig. 2-21; also 1-4). These are formed by particular chro-

Fig. 2-21. Cells of the watermelon, Citrullus vulgaris. Left, cell in interphase with a large nucleolus and numerous small chromocenters. Right, same cell in prophase with the nucleolus gone and the chromocenters showing up as the heterochromatic parts of individual chromosomes. (L. Geitler, Chromosomenbau, Berlin: Gebrüder Borntraeger, 1938, after Doutreligne.)

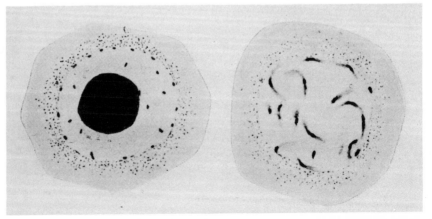

mosomes that have an active region called the *nucleolar organizer* (see Figs. 6-4 and 6-6), which in some as yet undetermined manner accumulates or manufactures nucleolar material and organizes it into a compact body. Chemically, the nucleolus is rich in proteins and ribose nucleic acids (RNA), and it seems likely that the RNA of the nucleolus passes into the cytoplasm to become attached to the ribosomes, where it participates in protein synthesis.

Analysis of the chromatin reveals the presence of four major components: deoxyribose nucleic acid (DNA), RNA, a protein of low molecular weight called *histone,* and a more complex protein. We have as yet no clear conception of how these four molecules are grouped together to form chromatin or a chromosome; we only know that DNA is the molecule of heredity within whose structure is coded, as on a magnetic tape, the information of inheritance that gives to the cell its unique qualities. The role of the other three molecules is uncertain, but we can hazard a guess that they provide the DNA with a high degree of stability and a means of performing its hereditary function. When we come to consider the cell in division we shall also see that DNA, as a molecule, is so constructed that it can duplicate itself time and again with a remarkable degree of exactitude.

Extracellular
Substances

The plasma membrane is generally considered to be the outer living limit of the cell, but not necessarily its outer boundary. We can see such outer boundaries most readily in plant cells, many of which possess heavy walls of cellulose, but animal cells and many unicellular organisms also exhibit a number of somewhat comparable external substances. To state categorically, however, that any part of the cell, either inside or on the immediate outside, is living or nonliving is to presume to define life, and as everyone knows, doing so has its pitfalls.

Most extracellular substances are proteins or polysaccharides, i.e., macromolecules formed by the linking together of smaller repeating molecular units. Often they combine with lipids and minerals to produce highly complex molecular structures. The functions these substances serve are varied: *water retention* in the case of the slimy secretions of many algae (agar is a commercially useful product derived from some algae); *protection* as provided by the tough, chitinous covering of insects; *support* as from the cellulose walls of plants, and from the *collagen* in cartilage and bone; *rigidity* and *hardness* as from the mineralized regions of bone, the dentine and enamel of teeth, the siliceous shells of diatoms, and chitin; *elasticity* as from the *elastin fibers* of skin or artery walls; and *adhesiveness* as from the *middle lamellae* of plants cells and the *hyaluronic acid* and *chondroitin sulfate* of animal cells. The *permeability* of cells is also governed in part by their extracellular substances. The slime secreted by amebae and other aquatic organisms can provide adhesion as well as act as a lubricating material for gliding along surfaces, while the outer character of bacterial cells determines, among other things, their immunological and virulent properties. The adhesiveness of cell surfaces is particularly critical, because without it cells would fall apart in dividing, hence multicellularity would be impossible.

The subject of extracellular substances, therefore, is a large and varied one, but here we shall restrict our discussion to those commonly found in higher plants and animals.

PLANT CELL WALLS

Figure 3-1 illustrates, in cross section, the wall of·a.typical plant cell found in stems, leaves, or roots. Adjacent cells share a layer known as the *middle lamella,* or intercellular substance. It forms the first partition between two cells as they arise through cell division and acts later as an *intercellular cement* binding cells together. It is not well understood, but it appears to consist mostly of *pectin,* a substance related to cellulose since it is also formed from sugars; most of us know pectin as the additive responsible for the "setting" of jellies. The *primary wall,* lying between the middle lamella and the plasma membrane, is a secretion product of the cytoplasm. While a cell is enlarging, this wall is thin, elastic, and capable of great extension. It consists principally of celluloses and sugars of various kinds, although some proteins are also present, and thickens only after the cell has ceased to enlarge. The *secondary wall* forms between the primary wall and the plasma membrane. It may be thick or thin and of varying degrees of hardness or color. It is the part of the cell that gives various woods and

Fig. 3-1. Typical wall structure of matured and lignified plant cells. Left, cross section showing arrangement of the various layers and the complex structure of the secondary wall; right, longitudinal section through a similar cell. (Reprinted with permission from K. Esau, Plant Anatomy. New York: Wiley, 1953.)

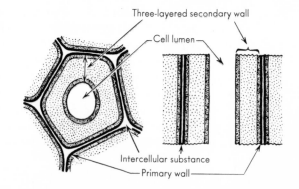

Three-layered secondary wall

Cell lumen

Intercellular substance

Primary wall

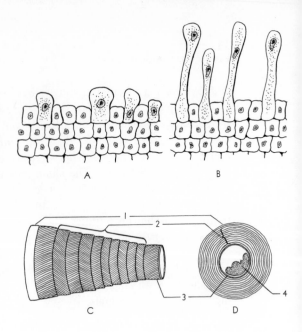

Fig. 3-2. Growth and structure of the cotton fiber. (A) Outer layer of cells of young cotton seed showing the beginning enlargement of the fibers on the day of flowering; (B) same, 24 hours later; (C) diagram of the various layers of cellulose laid down in a mature cotton fiber: (1) outer primary cell wall, (2) concentric inner layers revealing the different orientation of the cellulose in the secondary thickenings, (3) last inner layer of the secondary wall; (D) same, in cross section, with (4) representing the remains of cell contents. (Redrawn and modified from Brown and Ware, Cotton, 3rd ed. New York: McGraw-Hill, 1958.)

plant fibers (cotton, flax, hemp) their particular character, and from which is derived the cellulose used in the manufacture of rayon, nitrocellulose, cellophane, and certain plastics.

Let us examine the growth of the cotton fiber in order to illustrate the principles of cell-wall formation. The mature fiber, or lint as it is called, may be one-half to one-and-one-half inches in length. Located in the outermost layer of cells, or *epidermis,* of the seed coat (Fig. 3-2), each lint cell is attached to neighboring cells by a middle lamella and possesses a thin primary wall. On the day of flowering, the cell begins to elongate, a process that takes 13 to 20 days and terminates when the cell is 1000 to 3000 times as long as it is wide. The primary wall then ceases to elongate, and the secondary wall forms as sugars in the cytoplasm are converted into cellulose fibrils and deposited on the inside of the primary wall. The depositing of cellulose continues until the fruit is mature. The cell then dies, collapses, and flattens to give the fiber used in the manufacture of cotton threads and cloths.

Cellulose is a *macromolecule* built up of repeating units of sugar (glucose) into *microfibrils* that eventually reach sizes which are relatively large in the world of electron microscopy (Fig. 3-3). In cross section, the cotton fiber has an area of about 300 μ^2 and is made up of approximately one billion cellulose chains. These are grouped into *fibrils* of several orders of size, each one running the length of the entire fiber in a parallel, or sometimes helical (spiral), fashion. The spaces between the fibrils give the fiber its flexibility and allow for the complete penetration of dyes, whereas the parallel orientation of the fibrils accounts for its great tensile strength (nearly that of steel). It has been estimated that each cotton fiber contains about 10 trillion cellulose molecules, which are built up from approximately 60 quadrillion glucose molecules. Also, a single fiber is but one of many thousand growing on the surface of each cotton seed. From these rough calculations, we can gain some appreciation of the activity of plant cells in transforming carbon dioxide and water through photosynthesis into organic molecules; multiplying these molecules, the cell then builds them into an elaborate structure, the cell wall. The cell carries out the process of repeating molcules to form its structural elements—proteins, fats, nucleic acids, and polysaccharides—in much the same way man does to form plastics and synthetic fibers.

The organization of the cell wall also illustrates two sound construction principles. The strength of the cotton fiber, composed of pure cellulose, is gained by grouping the molecules into ever larger fibrils; this arrangement of parts is the principle of the construction of cables and ropes. Other types of cell walls, however, are impregnated with different substances. One of these is *lignin*, a complex, nonfibrous sugar derivative that forms in the spaces between the cellulose fibrils. This arrangement is also the principle of the reinforced concrete that is utilized in many of our modern buildings; the cellulose provides rods of high tensile strength and the lignin is a hard substance that is resistant to pressures. The cellulose need not, of course, be as well oriented as in the cotton fiber, and other substances, such as *cutin* and *waxes,* both derivatives of fatty acids, may replace lignin. In such instances, the strength of the wall is less, but the cell surface is water-repellant.

Fig. 3-3. Fibers of cellulose as formed in the wall of an algal cell. Each fiber would be composed of many small fibrils grouped as in a rope or cable (X 34,000).

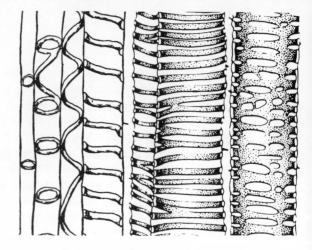

Fig. 3-4. Cells in the wood of higher plants exhibiting various patterns of secondary wall formation. The interrupted areas are thin enough to permit the passage of water and dissolved materials.

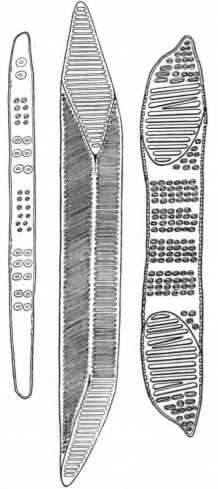

Fig. 3-5. Water-conducting cells in the xylem of higher plants that show different arrangements of pits on their side and end walls. Left, from sequoia; middle, from bracken fern; right, from alder.

Since most plant cells conduct water and dissolved substances as well as provide support, even, as in wood, after they have died, the heavy wall must be interrupted at intervals to allow for passage from one cell to another. Interruption occurs in a variety of ways, and as Fig. 3-4 indicates, the secondary wall may exist as rings, spiral bands, or sequences of thick and thin areas. Such gaps give flexibility as well as support and ease of conduction. In other cells, particular areas may be perforated by *pits,* or *pit fields,* or the end wall of a cell may be perforated or even missing to provide a connected column simulating a channel made up of short pieces of pipe (Fig. 3-5).

INTERCELLULAR SUBSTANCES OF ANIMAL CELLS

The intercellular "glue" of animal cells is principally of two kinds: *hyaluronic acid* and *chondroitin sulfate*. Collectively, these are known as *ground substances*.

Combined with protein and lacking sulfur, hyaluronic acid is a jelly-like, amorphous, viscous polysaccharide of high molecular weight. It is able to retain water tenaciously. Functionally, hyaluronic acid serves a number of purposes. As a "glue" it binds cells together at the same time that it permits flexibility; in the fluids of joints it acts as a lubricant and, possibly, as a shock absorber; in the fluids of the eye it may act to retain water and keep the shape of the eye fixed.

The viscosity of hyaluronic acid is determined, in part, by the amount of calcium present; for example, the cells of young embryos of sea urchins tend to fall away from one another if kept in a calcium-free medium, and developmental processes cannot proceed normally. Another point to note about hyaluronic acid is that it can be dissolved by an enzyme, *hyaluronidase;* this substance is present in sperm cells, and is readily formed by some bacteria. The action of the enzyme in sperm cells permits sperm to penetrate the jelly coat that surrounds an egg; without it the sperm could not bring about fertilization. The ability of some bacteria to manufacture the enzyme means that they can effectively invade tissues and so spread an infection from the initial point of entry.

Chondroitin sulfate is a firmer gel than hyaluronic acid, and, like the latter, it is a polysaccharide combined with proteins. It is particularly evident in *cartilage,* where it is associated with fibrous elements such as *collagen,* and where it provides a matrix in which the cartilage-forming cells are nestled (Fig. 3-6). The arrangement gives good support and adhesiveness while preserving a measure of flexibility (ears, nose, ends of ribs, new bones, respiratory tract, joints, etc.). Bone, in fact, appears first as a skeleton of cartilage, after which calcification of the intercellular substance takes place as one of the major processes of hardening.

The *basement membrane* is a somewhat more definitely organized and special ground substance. Found in a number of organs where it both binds cells together and helps to shape the particular organ, the basement membrane is prominent in skin. Here it lies between the epidermis and the dermis as a condensation of intercellular substances. Unlike ground substances in general, it may be highly laminated, as in amphibians (Fig. 3-7). There may be 20 or more laminae, with fibers in each lamina lying at right angles to the layers above and below it. Such an arrangement of fibers gives flexibility as well as strength.

The fibrous elements embedded in the ground substance are *collagen, elastin,* and *reticulin.* All are basically proteins of high molecular weight. It has been estimated that about one-third of the protein of a mammal is

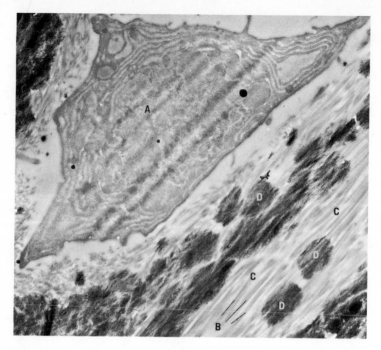

Fig. 3-6. Electron micrograph of an osteoblast, or bone-forming cell, and the surrounding extracellular material. A, osteoblast with a large central nucleus and a well-developed endoplasmic reticuum; B, collagen fibers; C, collagen fibers showing their characteristic axial periodicity every 640 A; D, collagen fibers beginning to decalcify, with the dark material being aggregates of individual apatite crystals of bone. (Courtesy Dr. Melvin Glimcher.)

collagen, and it is located in those areas where a degree of firmness or rigidity is needed (muscles, bone skin, tendons, etc.). Collagen can be readily dissolved in dilute acid. Dissolved collagen will reaggregate spontaneously in solution if conditions are suitable; presumably this is the manner of their aggregation outside of the cell in the ground substance.

Fig. 3-7. The basement membrane in amphibian skin, showing its laminated structure. The alternate layers are formed by collagen fibers running at right angles to one another. (Courtesy Dr. P. Weiss.)

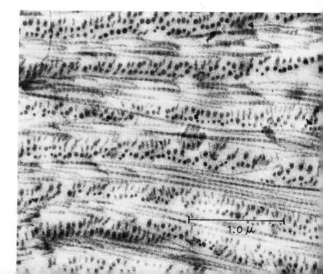

1.0 μ

Elastin and reticulin, unlike collagen, show no periodic structure. Elastin is a stringy protein that has the capacity, as its name suggests, to stretch and snap back into its original state, much as an elastic rubber band would. Consequently, it is prevalent where elasticity is required, as in skin, and the tissues surrounding the major blood vessels.

Reticulin consists of much finer fibers than do collagen and elastin, but is probably closely related to collagen in all ways except aggregation. The fibers are finely branched, are found generally in the ground substance, and are particularly abundant in the basement membrane.

INTERCELLULAR SUBSTANCES AND AGING

From what has been said it should be clear that ground substances and their associated fibers serve a number of purposes. Cells aggregate into organs of definite shape and size, and organ systems are tied together to form the intact and functioning organism. Adhesiveness, lubrication, rigidity, and elasticity are but some of the required features of a functioning organism that are governed by the quality and quantity of ground substance. If the character of the intercellular products changes, the organism itself must similarly change.

It now seems apparent that the process of aging is, in part, related to changes in the intercellular substances. All of us are familiar with some of these changes in a gross way: stiffening of joints, loss of elasticity in the skin, hardening of arteries, toughness and stringiness of a piece of old beefsteak. There is still uncertainty about the meaning of many of the alterations in ground substance that accompany aging, but it is at least clear that an increase in the amount and thickness of the collagen fibers occurs; that the elastic fibers become less springy and thicker, possibly because of an increased binding of calcium ions; and that the reticular fibers become heavier and more brush-like. If we consider that these fibers, so necessary to the organization of living systems during the course of development, continue to be formed after mature growth has been reached, then we can view aging, at least in part, as an aspect of development that has gone beyond the optimal needs of the organism for proper functioning. Acquiring multi-cellularity through the adhesiveness and preservation of cells, means, therefore, that aging is simultaneously introduced into the life history as an inevitable consequence wherever a determinative, or limited, type of growth is characteristic—as it is in animals. Single-celled organisms are potentially immortal, and the relatively long life of plants such as a tree is due not to the preservation of cells but rather to the discarding of old cells— to become wood, bark, and dead leaves—and the continued production of new cells. By contrast with animals, plants therefore, possess a more indeterminative type of growth.

Cells in General

CHAPTER FOUR

List, if you will, the organs of your body. Even if your knowledge of biology comes only from a casual reading of the daily newspaper or an occasional magazine, the list would be a substantial one: muscles, nerves, skin, eyes, and bones, to mention a few of the more obvious ones. Add, for good measure, examples from the plant world: the thorn of a rose, a wind-blown seed of the milkweed, the soft wood of balsa and the tough wood of oak, the needlelike leaf of the pine.

Clearly this is a miscellany of organs and structures, having little in common in outward appearances and in functions. Yet they share one feature: They are made up of cells and/or cell products. Equally obviously, however, the varied character of these structures must result from the varied character of the individual cells and cell products. Also, since each of the organisms possessing these structures must have arisen from a single fertilized egg cell, the varied character of the cells must have been acquired during the course of growth and development. We can scarcely help being impressed that the cell is a wonderfully plastic unit, capable of modifying itself as an organism matures. No sculptor or engineer has so versatile a medium with which to work.

It is, of course, impossible in a book of this size to deal with the many interesting problems of comparative cytology. Instead, we shall consider briefly the general problems of cell shape, size, and energy, and then, in a comparative way, examine a number of different kinds of cells to see how their function is related to their internal anatomy.

CELL SHAPE

Let us first look at organisms that are unicellular (Fig. 4-1). When we remember that cytoplasm is a viscous substance and that it is bounded by a semi-elastic outer membrane, we naturally assume that the shape of these self-sufficient cells would be spherical, since their surface tension, particularly in those that are free-floating, should form them in the same way that surface tension shapes air-borne soap bubbles.

Many cells, indeed, do have a spherical structure: the eggs of many

Fig. 4-1. Examples of cell shape among unicellular organisms.

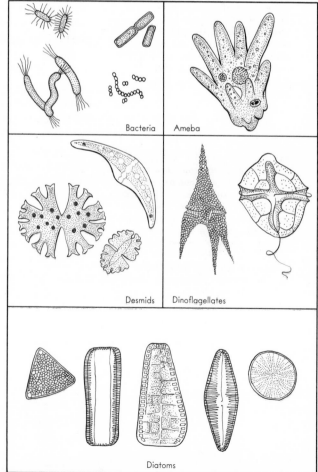

Bacteria Ameba

Desmids Dinoflagellates

Diatoms

Fig. 4-2. Acetabularia, the green alga that grows in warm marine waters. It is unicellular until it enters a reproductive stage, at which time the cap divides into reproductive cells. (Copyright by General Biological Supply House, Inc., Chicago.)

Fig. 4-3. Connective tissue cells grown in a plasma clot; their shapes are related to the number of outgrowths of cell membrane that adhere to the surface on which they are growing. At one extreme many outgrowths lead to a stellate shape (A); at the other, few outgrowths to a bipolar shape (E). (Courtesy Dr. P. Weiss, and reprinted from Oncley et al., Biophysical Sciences—A Study Program, Wiley, 1960.)

marine animals when released into the water, many yeasts and bacteria, and a variety of unicellular algae, among others. But from the different shapes attained by other forms of unicellular life, it appears certain that shape is an inherent, and an inherited, feature of the organism itself rather than that surface tensions or external forces exert a dominant effect. Some bacteria are rods, spirals, or even commas; among the algae, the diatoms, desmids, and dinoflagellates, with their unusual contours and outer skeletons, have a bizarre appearance (Fig. 4-1). Even the familiar ameba is not normally a sphere. Generally flattened because it rests on a surface, it has no particular shape, but is rather a fluid mass of protoplasm that can flow this way or that; only at rest or in death does it round up.

One of the most remarkable single-celled organisms is *Acetabularia,* an alga found in the warm marine waters (Fig. 4-2). Some species may be 9 to 10 cm.

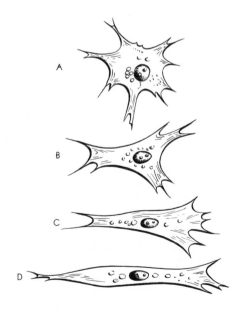

in height, and a distinctive cap, characteristic of each species, tops off the whole structure. Yet until it commences its fruiting stage, it is a single cell, with the nucleus residing at the base of the stalk in the rootlike *rhizoid*.

When we turn to a consideration of cell shapes in multicellular organisms, the most logical conclusion we can form is that shape results from the reaction of the cell to its environment. With animal cells, we can best judge this by examining the behavior of cells in tissue culture. Figure 4-3 represents five different connective tissue cells in dilute blood plasma. The cells are relatively free, and the form they assume at any given moment is related to the number of extensions of the plasma membrane, the extensions being points of adherence to a glass slide. A view of living cells through time-lapse cinematography reveals that the boundary of a cell is in a state of constant activity; extensions of the membrane are being formed, drawn back in, and then reformed ceaselessly. When these extensions are few, the cell has an elongated shape; when many, the cell is more or less stellate, with points extending from it. When, however, the plasma medium in which

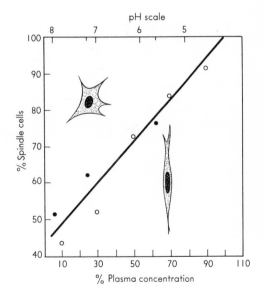

Fig. 4-4. Relation of cell shape to plasma (i.e. fiber) concentration (shown by dark circles) and to the degree of acidity (pH) (shown by open circles). (Courtesy Dr. P. Weiss, and reprinted with permission from Oncley et al. Biophysical Sciences—A Study Program, **Wiley, 1960.**)

the cells exist is made more concentrated or the acidity of the medium is increased (Fig. 4-4), more and more of the cells become bipolar rather than stellate because the fibers of protein found in the plasma become thicker and more numerous. These fibers restrict the cell, and tend to orient the direction in which the cell explores the environment through extension; elongation results.

In organized tissues, therefore, cell shape would result from neighboring contacts with other cells, and by the tensions exerted on the cell. When nearly spherical cells are packed together, however, they tend to become faceted as they come in contact with neighboring cells, much as the sides of soap bubbles become flattened when the bubbles are jammed together in a small space. In animals this phenomenon can be seen in the early stages of the development of an embryo (Fig. 4-5). The cell mass still retains for a brief period the rounded shape and size of the original egg, but in adjusting to the available space, the cells shape themselves accordingly. Similar arrangements of plant cells can be seen in the growing tips of roots or branches, in a potato tuber, or in the central pitch of an elderberry stem.

Cells are not always packed in the same way, of course. Some are layered in flat sheets, as in the skin or the linings of blood vessels. These naturally tend to be wider than they are deep, since the mechanics of stretching force them into such a shape. Muscles and bones are also

Fig. 4-5. The accommodation of cells in a given area requires that shape be modified if close packing is to be achieved. (A) Fertilized egg of a snail; (B) 4-cell stage of developing snail embryo; (C) 16-cell stage of the same snail, with no increase in the size of the embryo over that in (A) and (B); (D) Typical apical growing region of a plant; (E) Cells in the pith of an elderberry in cross section (left) and longitudinal section (right). Both sectional and surface faces of cell walls of the elderberry show openings (pits) between cells.

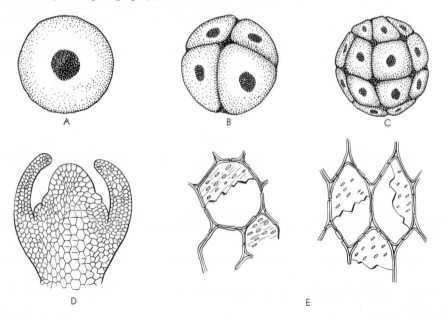

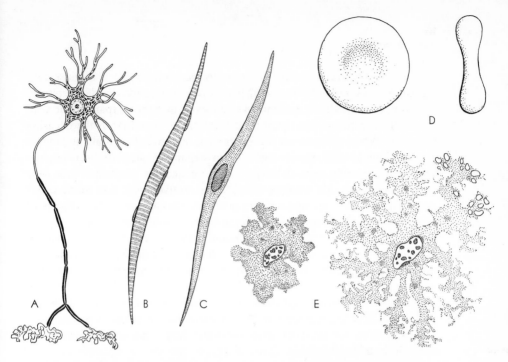

Fig. 4-6. Animals cells of different shapes: (A) nerve cell, with axon (long branch) and dendrites (the finer, small branches); the axon is encompassed by Schwann cells (see Fig. 2-6); (B) striated muscle cell; (C) smooth muscle cell; (D) human red blood cells, front and in cross section; (E) pigment-containing melanocyte, expanded and contracted.

elongated structures, oriented by growth stresses; their slender cells run parallel to the long axis of each respective organ.

It would be a mistake, however, to overemphasize the role of mechanical forces in shaping cells, because a cell's function and shape must be compatible with each other. Figure 4-6 illustrates four types of animal cell. The human red blood cell is spherical when viewed face on, flattened and concave when seen in cross-section. Its function, of course, is to transport oxygen from the lungs to the tissues, and carbon dioxide from the tissues to the lungs. Its thin dimensions permit it to exchange gases rapidly, while its rounded contours allow it to slide easily through even the smallest capillaries. A spherical cell would be useless in this respect, for the gas exchange between the exterior of the cell and its center would be very slow in proportion to its size.

The three long cells in Fig. 4-6 are examples of two types of muscle and and one type of nerve cell. The former contract violently when a muscle is in action, whereas the latter, which may reach over three feet in length in a human being, is part of an extensive communication network— the telephone system, if you will—for relaying messages throughout the body. Imagine, if you can, a nerve or muscle cell with a spherical or flat shape. Would it be able to perform its function efficiently?

The other two cells in Fig. 4-6 are *melanocytes,* so-called because they contain a black pigment, *melanin,* that is responsible for the dark color in the skins of animals. A melanocyte can exist in either expanded or contracted form, and can transform itself from one to the other as the occasion demands. When melanocytes are contracted, an animal such as the chameleon or flounder will appear light; when expanded, with its branches extended, the animal appears darker. The melanocyte, therefore, not only gives color to the skin but also provides protective coloration that enables an animal to blend into either a light or a dark background. The capacity of the cell to alter its shape is, therefore, in keeping with its function.

The cellulose walls of mature plant cells do not permit a similar flexibility of shape. Once fully mature, the shape of such a cell is more or less permanently fixed. Prior to maturity, however, and when they are in a formative stage, plant cells are also influenced by their environment. Epidermal cells on the surface of leaves are flattened laterally, those in potato tubers or in elderberry pith are faceted by the pressure of adjoining cells, and those for the conduction of water and solutes are elongated as roots or branches elongate.

Plainly, environment is determinative in cell shape. On the other hand, we must remember that the character of a cell, including its shape, is also influenced by control through the nucleus. A cell of a pine tree is different from that of an oak tree, although they may carry out the same functions and be subjected to the same environmental influences. How character is determined by inheritance, however, is a vastly complicated problem, and we have relatively little basic information on the step-by-step development of final form.

CELL SIZE

The sizes of cells vary widely, as we can see if we choose cells at random from the plant and animal kingdoms. The smallest cells visible under a light microscope are bacteria (0.2 to 5.0 μ), and the very smallest of these lie just at the limits of resolution. The largest cell of all is the egg of the ostrich, which measures about 6 inches around the outside and about 3 inches (75 mm) when the shell is removed. The ratio of linear dimensions between the largest and smallest cells is about 75,000:1; the ratio of their volumes is about $75,000^3:1$. The order of difference is the same as that between a sphere an inch in diameter and one more than a mile wide.

It now appears that the smallest cell, or free-living organism, is not a bacterium; it is so minute it could never have been "seen" except through an electron microscope. Louis Pasteur discovered the *existence* of this organism, which is the causative agent of pleuropneumonia, a contagious disease of cattle. But Pasteur was unable to isolate, culture, or see it under a microscope; it was too small. There are a number of kinds of this organism, but the smallest is about 0.1 micron in diameter, and is known as PPLO (pleuropneumonia-like organism), or *Mycoplasma* (Fig. 4-7). In size these cells are like viruses in that they can pass through a fine-pored filter; they can, however, grow in a nonliving medium, as do bacteria. Their internal organization is also bacteria-like: plasma membrane, ribosomes, complete metabolic machinery with some 40 known enzymes, and an ill-defined nuclear apparatus lacking a nuclear membrane. Whether there are other cells of similar dimensions remaining to be discovered is a moot question.

The range of cell size in the human body extends from the nearly spherical *small leucocyte* (white blood cell), with a diameter of 3 to 4 μ, to the nerve cell, the axon of which may be over three feet in length. In inches, the range is 3/25,000 to 36, or a ratio of 1:300,000 for the longest dimension. Such a comparison is misleading, however, for the main body of the nerve cell (Fig. 4-6) is not nearly so different in size (100 μ) from that of the small leucocyte. The ratio, in fact, when computed on this basis, is about 30:1. But even this comparison has little meaning without a consideration of the factors governing size. A hen's egg, for instance, with outside dimensions of 60 $\times$ 45 mm, is large because it stores food in an enormous yolk for the developing embryo; a human embryo, on the other hand, draws its nutrients from its mother so the egg has little need for a large reserve of food; the egg's size is commensurate with its nutritive needs, for it is about 0.1 mm in diameter.

Nerve, muscle, and blood cells have different sizes, which are related to the particular tasks performed. With cells of similar function we find that three factors tend to govern size: (1) the nucleocytoplasmic ratio, (2) the

Fig. 4-7. Schematic drawing of the morphology of a PPLO, with outer plasma membrane, a double helix of chromatin material, ribosomes (larger spheres) and other dissolved substances (smaller spheres). The diameter of this cell is about 0.1 micron.

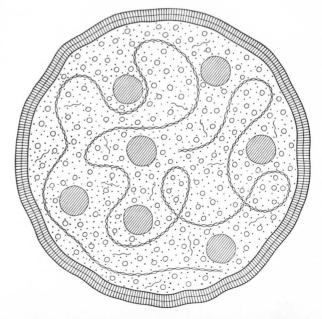

ratio of cell surface area to cell volume, and (3) the rate of cellular activity or metabolism. Although these factors are obviously interrelated, since each involves surface-area considerations, for convenience we shall consider them separately.

We have already mentioned that the nucleus is the controlling center of the cell. In cooperation with the cytoplasm, the nucleus regulates the growth, development, and continued existence of the cell, and although a cell can function for a time without a nucleus, the cytoplasm will soon become like an assembly production line without control and cease to operate. The nucleus, however, cannot exercise control over an indefinitely large amount of cytoplasm because as the cell enlarges, the surface area of the nucleus, across which an interchange of materials must pass, increases only with the square of the cell radius (area of a sphere $= 4 \pi r^2$), while the cell volume increases with the cube (volume $= 4/3 \pi r^3$). A disproportionate increase of cytoplasm would probably soon put the cell out of metabolic kilter. The area of the nucleus can be increased by a change of shape, or its volume can be doubled by doubling the number of *chromosomes,* the main components of the nucleus. Most mature cells, however, maintain a relatively constant nucleocytoplasmic ratio, while growing cells divide to keep the ratio below a certain maximum value.

The second limitation in a cell's size is the amount of surface area. Metabolism, of course, occurs continuously throughout the entire cell mass, but the substances required for metabolism can only pass in and out of the cells through the surface membranes. Oxygen, for example, is required by virtually all cells. If sufficient oxygen is to reach the center of the cell, its concentration outside the cell has to be at or above a certain critical value. This value is determined by the ease with which oxygen passes into the cell, the rate at which it is used per unit quantity of protoplasm, and the cell's dimensions. An equation can be set up to express this relationship; in it, the rate of utilization of oxygen and its diffusibility are in terms of simple proportion, whereas cell size, or area, is expressed as a square. Therefore, if the radius of a cell is doubled, the area of the cell will be the square of this value. Consequently, if air, which is 20 per cent oxygen, just supplies the center of a cell 0.1 mm in diameter with sufficient oxygen to keep it metabolizing normally, it would take pure oxygen to supply a similar flow to a cell with a diameter of 0.23 mm. Thus, for an increase in diameter of $\sqrt{5}$, or 2.3, a cell must receive 5 times the amount of oxygen at its outer boundary.

Since the surface area increases by the square of the radius and the volume increases as its cube, the volume is governed by the ability of the surface to provide the interior with the necessities demanded of it in metabolism; if the volume is too large, the center cannot function properly. These limitations can, however, be overcome in a variety of ways. Cells alter their spherical shape by flattening, folding, or elongating; thus their surface area can be increased without an increase in volume (Fig. 2-5). The flow of substances in or out can be similarly increased, and larger dimensions tolerated without interference with metabolic rates, so long as the expansion does not drastically alter the nucleocytoplasmic ratio.

We have discussed the surface problem as though the plasma membrane were a simple barrier across which substances pass according to simple laws of diffusion. For gases such as oxygen this is probably true. For other substances, however, the plasma membrane behaves as a "pump," moving these substances against a concentration gradient. For example, potassium can be concentrated in a cell when the outside concentration is low, while at the same time sodium is moved to the extracellular space where its concentration is high. The plasma membrane is actively engaged in this process, for enzymes in it perform this transport, the energy being derived from ATP.

The surface-volume dilemma appears to have been resolved time and time again in living organisms. A nerve cell, for example, may reach a yard in length, yet the cell body is not especially large, and the axons and dendrites are so tenuous they present no problem for the rapid exchange of materials across their surfaces. For the cells that cannot reach larger proportions, however, an increase in number rather than size is the only solution. An organ of the body (as opposed to a single cell) may be variously constructed in order to meet the demands assigned to it. In mammals, for example, the digestive system is a long coiled tube, and its inner absorptive lining is composed of many convoluted surfaces made up of small columnar or cuboidal cells arranged much as is the piling on a bath towel (Fig. 2-5). The surface area is, as a result, enormously increased. The inner surface of the lungs is also designed to facilitate the rapid exchange of oxygen and carbon dioxide; each cell is in contact with a blood vessel on one side and air on the other.

Plant cells differ markedly from animal cells in the manner by which surface-volume problems are solved. Their rigid cell walls preclude drastic shape changes and, consequently, an increase in surface without an increase in volume. Internal rearrangements of organelles, however, accomplish the same end. Large central vacuoles are characteristic of plant cells, and these push the cytoplasm as a thin layer to the outer edge of the cell, where a rapid exchange of nutrients or gases is possible (Fig. 2-17).

The third factor related to the size of a cell is the rate of activity carried on inside it. Although cell size is not absolutely correlated with the rate of metabolism, the rapidly metabolizing cells of such organisms as bacteria, hummingbirds, shrews, bees, flies, and mosquitoes are generally smaller than those of the more slowly metabolizing animals such as men, elephants, amphibians (frogs, toads, etc.), and grasshoppers. The surface exchanges in the cells of the smaller, more active animals must be accomplished more rapidly, and the cells must thus be smaller in order to attain the greatest amount of surface area relative to volume. If this were not the case, the metabolic processes would bog down. For example, if the elephant metabolized at the same rate as the hummingbird, it would roast itself, because the tremendous amount of heat it would generate could not escape. The same result would occur if a human egg cell metabolized at the same rate as a small bacterial cell.

Cell size can also be viewed as a problem in structural engineering. Protoplasm is a viscous substance that needs support of some kind to keep it hanging together and functioning as it should. Units of it are thus confined within the area of the cell by these membranes about 100 A thick that form the elastic but firm boundary of the cell. Since cells of minute dimensions would make inefficient use of this support, and oversize cells, because of internal pressure, would burst like punctured balloons, a balance must be maintained between the need for support and the need for a proper surface-volume relationship.

What, then, is the optimum size of a cell? Obviously there is no simple answer, for size is related to what the cell does, and function is related to both the character and rate of metabolism. Figure 4-8 shows a number of different cells of a graded scale of size, with the bacterial virus and the hemoglobin molecule added for comparative purposes. Since each of these cells exists we must assume that each in its own way is efficient. If we excluded eggs from our consideration—the yolk-containing kind really belong in a category by themselves—we find few cells that exceed 100 μ in diameter (Acetabularia is a striking exception), whereas the minimum is about 0.1 μ, a ratio of 1000:1. (We have also excluded viruses because, whether they are considered to be cells or not, their energy for metabolism is derived from the cells they parasitize.) If we were to hazard a guess at this time, we could say that maximum size is probably limited by structural considerations, and by the need to maintain an adequate flow of substances and energy in, out, and within cells; minimum size, however, must be limited by the space necessary to contain the minimum apparatus for self-sustaining life: DNA, RNA, and the proteins needed for enzymatically controlled reactions. Clearly, the cell diameter must exceed 200 A, otherwise there would be no space between plasma membranes. Other considerations suggest 500 A, or about one-half the diameter of a PPLO cell, as the minimal diameter. Cells of this size, however, have not yet been found.

COMPARATIVE CYTOLOGY

In considering cellular structure, and cell shapes and sizes, we have, of course, viewed cells in a comparative way. The comparisons, however, have been indirect, and you have had to draw conclusions for yourself. Here we wish to confront the subject directly, and to do so in two ways: (1) by comparing selected cells within a given organism—a vertebrate—

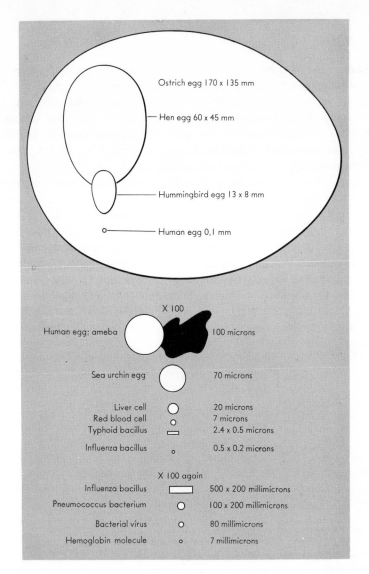

Fig. 4-8. A scale of sizes of different kinds of cells, with the bacterial virus and the hemoglobin molecule included for comparative purposes. The ostrich egg and the eggs within it are here reduced by one-half.

to show how the special functions relate to the development of one or more structural features, and (2) by comparing cells of the vertebrate with those of other organisms that have internal structures which are markedly different.

Before dealing with comparisons, however, we need to focus our attention on the central fact that *all cells are instruments of energy transformation,* and that structural differences are closely correlated with the ways energy is obtained and the use it is put to. The chemical details of energy relationships are the subject of another volume in this series,* so our discussion here will be couched only in general terms.

We have earlier referred to the cell as a factory. And we know that this factory may have many sizes and shapes, and may perform either general or specialized functions. Its internal structure must be consistent with the tasks demanded of it. The energy problems, however, are basically similar in most cells.

Figure 4-9 is a schematic representation of simple factory operations in terms of energy input and output. The fuel is generally coal or oil, the energy being locked up in chemical bonds. During combustion, O_2 is utilized and the energy is released as heat. The heat, in turn, makes steam to drive a generator, thereby converting heat energy into electrical energy. The waste products are CO_2 and H_2O. Electricity, in the form of electrons (*e*) flowing through wires, performs work of three basic kinds: *mechanical work,* or lifting; *transport,* or moving materials from one place to another; and *assembly,* or manufacture.

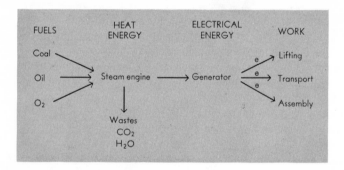

Fig. 4-9. Schematic representation of the flow of energy in a typical factory, from its bound form as fuel to its final utilization to do work. The letter e represents electrical energy in the form of electrons flowing along a wire. Compare with Fig. 4-10.

The cell is basically similar in operation, but with one major exception: It cannot use heat to do work since it functions at a low and relatively constant temperature. The primary source of energy is the sun; chloroplasts capture light energy and transform it into chemical energy. All other energy resides in the chemical bonds of molecules.

Figure 4-10 depicts the basic steps in the energy cycle of the cell. The fuels are carbohydrates, fats, and proteins that in the presence of O_2 are broken down into smaller units in the mitochondria. As in our factory, the wastes are CO_2 and H_2O, but in the cell the chemical energy of the fuels

* W. D. McElroy, *Cell Physiology and Biochemistry.*

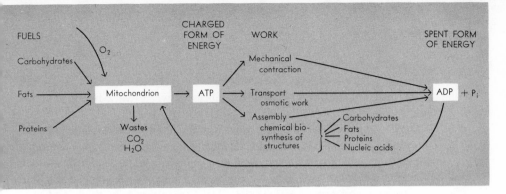

Fig. 4-10. Schematic representation of the flow of energy in a cell, from the combustible fuels to its ultimate utilization for specific kinds of work. ATP and ADP ($+P_i$) are, respectively, the charged and spent forms of energy.

is repackaged as chemical energy, and is not dissipated as heat. As a *charged form of energy,* the molecule ATP can yield its energy to other parts of the cell, and work can be performed. The tasks again are comparable in nature to those performed by our factory: mechanical work, as when muscles contract; transport, as when substances are moved from one area to another, often across membranes and against concentration gradients; and assembly, or the biosynthesis of other molecules and cellular structures. Energy, of course, is used to do this work, and in the process ATP is degraded into ADP (adenosine diphosphate) and inorganic phosphate (P_i). ADP and P_i are *spent forms of energy;* to be recharged, they pass back into the mitochondria where they emerge once again as ATP. The cycle must go on constantly in the living cell, and it has been estimated that a molecule of ATP in an active cell is recycled every 50 seconds.

The cells we wish now to consider are those capable of performing specifically the several kinds of word depicted in Fig. 4-10.

Contractive Cells

Mechanical work, or contraction, can be either sudden and violent or more gentle and continuous: the throwing of a baseball as opposed to rhythmic motion of breathing; the wink of an eyelid as opposed to the slow contractions of the stomach and intestines during digestion. Two kinds of cell perform these two kinds of contraction.

Striated, or *striped,* muscle cells are capable of sudden contraction; like a muscle itself, the cells are elongated and tapered, and are multinucleate (Fig. 4-6). The individual cells may be from 1 to 40 mm in length, and from 10 to 40 μ in width; their several nuclei, found at the outer edge of a cell, are apparently needed to control this large mass of cytoplasm. Each cell is covered with a thin, tough membrane, the *sarcolemma.* Internally, the cytoplasm consists primarily of longitudinal filaments, called *myofibrils,* arranged systematically; they appear under an electron microscope as alternating light and dark areas (Fig. 4-11). Different bands are clearly distinguishable, and one block of myofibrils between two Z bands is known as a *sarcomere*.

During contraction the sarcomeres become shorter and broader, thereby shortening the cell. The united action of many cells, coordinated by nerve impulses, causes the whole muscle to contract, and thus perform work. The myofibrils are the agents of contraction. When viewed in both longitudinal and cross section, the fibrils are alternately thick and thin. Both types are protein, the former being *myosin,* the later *actin.* The fibrils apparently oscillate back and forth rather constantly along the long axis of the cell, but that movement can be counteracted by the formation of chemical cross-links between the fibrils. When cross-links form between myosin and actin, the thick fibrils cause the thin ones to contract, and thus shorten both fibers and cell. The number of cross-links at any given time is related to the amount of ATP present. Thus, when the amount of ATP is high, and the energy available is within the ATP molecule, the cross-links are few in number; when ATP is split to ADP and P_i and energy is released, the linkage is high. The following relationship thereby holds:

1) energy spent
2) cross-links formed
3) contraction of actin

$$APT \rightleftharpoons ADP + P_i$$

1) energy charged
2) cross-links broken
3) relaxation of actin

The actual details of how these actions are accomplished is still not entirely clear, but it appears that most types of cellular movement—beating of cilia and flagella, movements of microvilli and amebae—occur in a comparable manner, i.e., by contractile proteins. The molecules of ATP must, of course, be plentiful and ready at hand when needed. The numerous and large mitochondria found adjacent to the sarcomeres (Fig. 4-11) represent ready sources of energy, and fit the muscle cell for its task.

Smooth muscles, in contrast, are found, for example, in the walls of arteries, veins, uterus and digestive tract (Fig. 4-6); and they contract involuntarily and rhythmically. The size of the individual cells is smaller than those of striated muscle, they are uninucleate, and they lack the tough sarcolemma of a striated cell. The striations so characteristic of the other muscle cells are also missing or few in number, and the myofibrils, although present, are very thin in diameter and apparently quite long, running the length of the cell. Presumably contraction occurs in the manner described

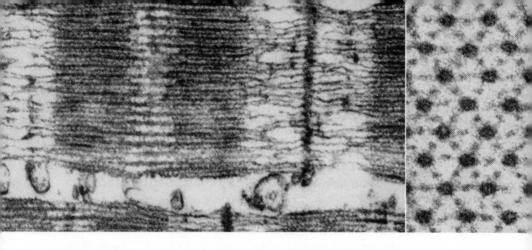

Fig. 4-11. Electron micrographs of portions of a striated muscle cell. Left, a sarcomere, i.e., the region between the two Z bands (the thin, dark bands at left and right), with mitochondria between adjacent sarcomeres. Right, cross section through a sarcomere, showing an end view of the filaments and their definite arrangement; the larger, darker ones are myosin, and each is surrounded by six lighter strands of actin.

for a striated cell, but since contraction is slow and gentle, the engery requirements are less demanding. Mitochondria are consequently less conspicuous in size and number.

If we now view muscle cells in terms of work performed, we can appraise their structure more meaningfully. The mitochondria are far more numerous in striated than in smooth cells, but in each type of cell their number and size are related to the cellular demands for energy. The mature muscle cells require no substantial amount of machinery for assembly or biosynthesis of materials other than ATP, so the endoplasmic reticulum, ribosomes, and Golgi apparatus form relatively inconspicuous, but by no means indispensable, elements in the over-all economy of these cells. The myofibrils, on the other hand, are our first encounter with this kind of an organelle; their contractile capacity, however, is peculiarly suited to the kind of work involved, and since mechanical work (contraction) is the main function of these cells, the myofibrils loom large as a structural and functional element.

Transporting Cells

In a vertebrate there are two principal cellular transporting systems: (1) the cells of the lining of the digestive tract, which move food from the lumen of the intestine into the blood stream, and (2) the cells of the kidney, which extract wastes and fluid from the blood stream and excrete them as urine. The cells of both systems are comparable, at least in their grosser aspects, and we need consider only those of the kidney, since we have already depicted the columnar absorbing cell of the intestine (Fig. 2-5).

Transport is not a passive effort; it requires energy. We would expect therefore to find numerous mitochondria in cells engaged in active and constant transport; and indeed they are large in both number and size. Since the rate of movement of materials in and out of the cells is, in part, a function of the amount of cell surface, we would also expect to find various modifications of the plasma membrane. The microvilli on one side of the cell, and the deep indentations of the membrane at the opposite side, provide such an increase in surface area (Fig. 4-12). In fact, it has been calculated that in one part of a kidney tubule, there are about 6500 microvilli per cell, thus increasing the surface area approximately 40 times.

The microvilli face the interior of the lumen of the tubule. Their function is absorption (some cells with microvilli secrete substances, however, so absorption may not be the only function of microvilli), and they reabsorb water and food materials such as dissolved sugars and salts from the urinary liquid passing down the tubule. Passing through the cell, the water and sugars leave the cell at its opposite end, through the infolded membranes at the base where capillaries abound. Water and food are thus reclaimed, but wastes pass on. In addition, however, the cells lining the tubules secrete substances into the lumen. The molecular traffic in kidney cells, therefore, is two-way. The structure of the cell is consistent with these activities, and since the degree of absorption and secretion varies along the tubule, the number of microvilli and the frequency of the deep folds in the basal membranes vary from cell to cell. Since movement of materials across these membranes requires energy, the number and size of the mitochondria also vary.

Fig. 4-12. Electron micrograph of the basal (inner) side of an epithelial cell of a kidney tubule, showing the deep involutions of the plasma membrane and the numerous, closely associated, mitochondria (M). The basement membrane (BM) is indicated. The opposite end of this cell, facing the lumen of the kidney tubule, would possess many microvilli. (Courtesy Dr. D. Fawcett.)

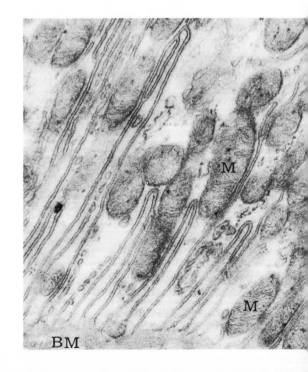

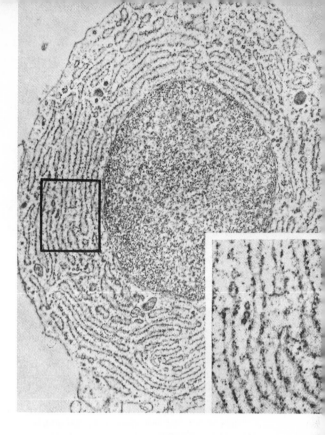

Fig. 4-13. Electron micrograph of a plasma cell (X 13,250) which produces antibodies; the antibodies are exported by the cell and enter the general circulatory system of the body. The inset is a higher magnification (X 31,680) of the endoplasmic reticulum. (Courtesy Ham and Leeson, Histology, 4th ed., 1961; with permission of Lippincott Co.)

The Golgi apparatus, the endoplasmic reticulum, and ribosomes are present, but as in the muscle cells, they are not conspicuous elements occupying large portions of the cell volume.

Assembly Cells

A great many cells are specialized for the biosynthesis of certain substances: pancreatic cells form and secrete digestive juices; outer skin cells, keratin; plasma cells, antibodies; and erythroblasts, hemoglobin. These substances are all proteins, and from what we know of protein synthesis, we would assume that substantial amounts of cytoplasmic RNA must be present to carry out this task. Figure 4-13 is an electromicrograph of a *plasma cell,* and the richness of the rough endoplasmic reticulum is evident. But contrast the cell in this figure and those in Fig. 2-8, which are secretory cells, with that in Fig. 4-14, which depicts a *proerythroblast,* an immature red blood cell. It, too, synthesizes a protein, hemoglobin, but its cytoplasm is strikingly free of the membranes of the endoplasmic reticulum although rich in ribosomal particles containing RNA. The erythroblast also possesses a meager amount of Golgi membranes, whereas the plasma and pancreatic cells show a normal Golgi apparatus.

The contrasting differences here are probably related to the fate of the synthesized material. In the erythroblast, the hemoglobin remains within the cell; no further transformation or transportation of it is necessary. The

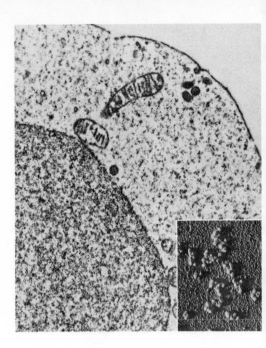

Fig. 4-14. Electron micrographs of a proerythroblast (immature red blood cell, or RBC) (X 17,280) and of the polyribosomes (X 43,200) (lower right) which manufacture hemoglobin. The nucleus is at the lower right. (Courtesy Dr. A. Ham and Leeson, Histology, 4th ed., 1961; with permission of Lippincott Co., Philadelphia; inset, courtesy J. R. Warner, A. Rich, and C. E. Hall.)

Fig. 4-15. Electron micrograph of a cell in the actively dividing roottip of maize. Several clumps of Golgi membranes can be seen above the nucleus, with a plastid near them; the mitochondria are few and scattered; the ER consists of long, slender membranes and with few, if any, attached ribosomes; pores are evident in the nuclear membrane and the chromosomes show no distinctive structure. At this magnification, the free ribosomes in the cytoplasm are not clearly defined, but are present in substantial amounts. The primary wall and middle lamella can also be seen, with the latter most evident at the angles as the darker material. (Courtesy Dr. G. Whaley.)

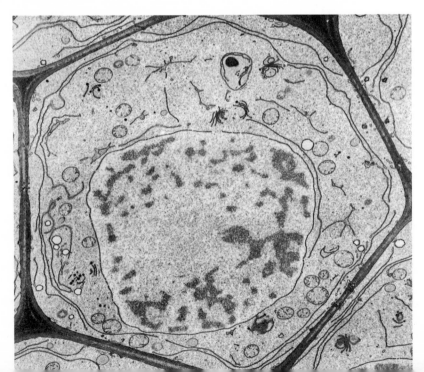

plasma and pancreatic cells, however, prepare their protein poducts for delivery outside the cell; these products are apparently transformed and repackaged. From what we now know, it seems likely that the repackaging is a function of the membranous endoplasmic reticulum and the Golgi apparatus. Once again, therefore, we find that the functions performed by the cell and its internal architecture are consistent, and this consistency permits us to interpret function in terms of structure, and vice versa.

Figures 2-9 and 4-15 provide a further contrast. Figure 2-9 is a cell from the testis of an opossum, and its principal function is the production of a steroid hormone. There is little morphological evidence of either bound or free RNA, and none expected since protein synthesis is not involved. The smooth endoplasmic reticulum, however, is believed to contain the enzymes for steroid synthesis, and it is consequently prominently developed. Figure 4-15, on the other hand, is an unspecialized cell from a rapidly dividing tissue. Such a cell has all the organelles—the centrosome is missing since this is a plant cell—but no one element is emphasized at the expense of any other. However, since cells of this type are rapidly growing and dividing, and consequently manufacturing more nuclear and cytoplasmic materials, an abundance of unbound RNA is characteristic.

PROTOCELLS

The cells we have been considering generally are *true cells,* or *eucells.* They are distinguished by the grouping of their principal hereditary materials into a membrane-bound nucleus. On the other hand, some cells, called *protocells,* lack such a nucleus, although they contain a "nuclear" substance and an outer, limiting plasma membrane. Whether they are more primitive than eucells, as their name would suggest, is debatable, but their distinctive characteristics set them apart. Protocells are found principally in the bacteria and blue-green algae.

Figure 4-16 depicts a bacterial species as seen in a light microscope.

Fig. 4-16. Cells of Bacillus cereus **stained by the Feulgen method to show the nuclear area. (Courtesy Dr. C. F. Robinow.)**

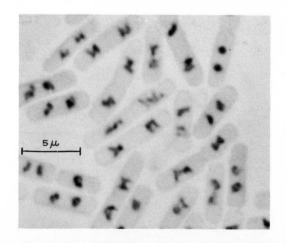

Fig. 4-17. Electron micrograph of a germinating spore of Bacillus subtilis, showing cell wall, darker plasma membrane, light nuclear area, and a relatively undifferentiated cytoplasm (X 57,200). (Courtesy Dr. C. F. Robinow.)

Fig. 4-18. Electron micrograph of a portion of a cell of Bacillus mycoides, showing a cytoplasmic, membranous inclusion that apparently has its origin in infoldings of the plasma membrane (X 186,660). (Courtesy Dr. C. F. Robinow.)

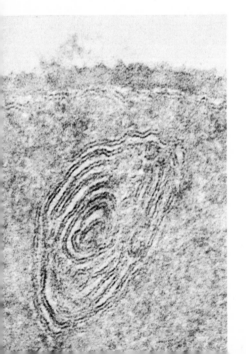

Staining procedures reveal a nuclear "area," but little else in the way of internal architecture. Higher magnification by means of electron microscopy reveals additional details (Fig. 4-17). The nuclear area, unbounded by a membrane, has a low electron density and is therefore relatively light in appearance, but the fine filaments are the hereditary material (DNA) of the cell. The cytoplasm contains some membranous structures (Fig. 4-18), possibly comparable to the ER of higher cells, and is richly packed with free particles containing RNA.

The cells of a blue-green algae are somewhat more highly organized. The chromatin of the nucleus is not limited by a membrane, but numerous membranes in the cytoplasm represent the photosynthetic lamellae. However, these membranes are not grouped into distinct chloroplasts.

We can, therefore, visualize a series of cells possessing an increasingly more complex set of organelles. The bacteria are the least complex, the blue-green algae a step above them in this regard, and then the true cells of more advanced plants and animals. Whether this sequence represents the stages of evolution in the de-

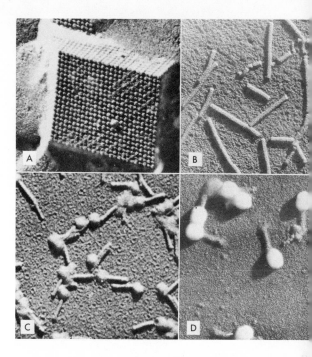

Fig. 4-19. Electron micrographs of viruses (A) Tobacco necrosis virus; the virus particles are spherical in shape and about 250 A in diameter, but when precipitated in ammonium sulfate they form a crystalline structure. (B) Tobacco mosaic virus; each rod is made up of a stack of plates similar to a stack of coins, with a protein coat on the outside and an inner core of ribose nucleic acid. (C) P2 bacteriophage of bacterial virus, which attacks the colon bacterium; each is equipped with a somewhat hexagonal head and a tail. (D) T6 bacteriophage, which also attacks the colon bacterium. (Courtesy Dr. L. W. Labaw.)

velopment of cells is an open question, but the sequence, as postulated, is a logical one.

VIRUSES

While on the subject of comparative cytology, we should consider the viruses. They are living organisms, but they are not cells. Over three hundred different viruses are known. Many of them are infective agents in such diseases as yellow fever, rabies, poliomyelitis, smallpox, mumps, and measles in human beings, and in a wide variety of diseases in plants and other animals. Figure 4-19 shows several viruses as they appear in the electron microscope.

The metabolism and structure of viruses differ from that of cells with which we are acquainted. A virus, for example, is not a free-living organism; it can grow and multiply only within another cell which it has parasitized. In some manner, the virus can alter the metabolic machinery of the cell so that it is directed toward making more virus instead of performing its usual functions. Otherwise, though, viruses are clothed with all the characteristics of life: they grow, multiply to produce exact replicas of themselves, and possess a type of inheritance not far different from our own. They also contain the key molecules of protein and nucleic acid invariably found in every living organism. The closest comparison that we can make between viruses and cells—if such a comparison is legitimate—is that the viruses are cells without cytoplasm; they possess little more than the nuclear hereditary apparatus.

The Cell
in Division

William Bateson, the great English geneticist of an earlier generation, once wrote: "The greatest advance I can conceive in biology would be the discovery of the instability which leads to the continued division of the cell. When I look at a dividing cell I feel as an astronomer might do if he beheld the formation of a double star: that an original act of creation is taking place before me."

Every biologist who has ever watched a living cell divide, or visualized the process when observing stained cells, has been as fascinated as was Bateson. Indeed, without too great a stretch of the imagination, we can characterize the movements of the chromosomes, their meticulous partitioning into daughter cells, and the segmentation of the cytoplasm as an exquisite minuet. With another cell division, the minuet commences all over again with but little variation. The meaning of the dance will become clear as we consider the cell in division in this and the next chapter.

Each of us developed from a single cell; this cell came from our parents, each of whom was formed from a single cell, and so on back to the beginning of cellular life. Our heritage from the past and our living extension into the future constitute a slender but unbroken series of perfectly formed, individual cells. They are perfect in the sense that, although they may vary among themselves, they are able to live, reproduce, and give rise to new cells and hence to new individuals.

The ways new cells originate have received extensive investigation and debate ever since the cellular nature of organisms was realized. The cell theory, of course, formally recognized that the cell is the basic unit of biological organization and function. Yet not until the middle of the nineteenth century was it generally accepted that cells originate through the division of pre-existing cells. We attribute this idea to the German, Rudolf Virchow, who stated in 1858:

> Where a cell exists there must have been a pre-existing cell just as the animal arises only from an animal and the plant only from a plant. The principle is thus established, even though the strict proof has not yet been produced for every detail, that through the whole series of living forms, whether entire animal or plant organisms or their component parts, there are rules of eternal law and continuous development, that is, of continuous reproduction.

Although we cannot reconstruct the beginnings of life from what we know today, presumably it did not begin in the form of the cells that we now see under our microscopes. They are the products of ages of evolution. Nor can life be originated anew; it is only spawned from pre-existing life. This theory, known as *biogenesis,* we credit to Louis Pasteur (1822–1895), although the Italian, Redi (1626–1698) had discovered the same thing two centuries before. Pasteur was not particularly concerned with the reproduction of cells, yet he demonstrated that the spontaneous generation of life could not occur under the conditions existing on earth today. He took two flasks of broth and boiled them, killing all the organisms in them. One flask he left open; the other he stoppered and made airtight. Within a few days the open flask contained bacteria, yeast, or molds of some sort, which, of course, were borne in the air; under the microscope it is clear that these germs, as we call them, consist of cells of various sorts. The stoppered flask, however, contained no life whatsoever, and could not until air was once more admitted. Yet air could be passed through the filter without contaminating the flask, provided the air was filtered of all organisms. These experiments, simple though they were, had far-reaching consequences because they disproved once and for all the idea that life can be created under present conditions; Pasteur and Virchow thus definitely established that life in a cellular form can only come from pre-existing life which also has a cellular form.

Man consists of approximately 10^{14} cells. Not only must these be formed and differentiated as the body matures, they must also, in many instances, be constantly replaced as they pass through their life cycle and die. In fact, within any healthy organism that grows or requires repair, the process of cell division produces new cells at the rate and for the period of time demanded by the organism at its particular age and in its particular environment. Not all cells, of course, divide at the same rate; some, indeed, cannot be replaced if lost. These cells eventually and inevitably die.

One of the most remarkable phenomena of nature, however, is that in all organisms the process of cell division is essentially the same. Thus if we describe this process as it takes place in one or two kinds of cell, we can see how it operates in the whole gamut of living organisms. This universal drama of cell division centers largely in the nucleus, but we must not forget that the cytoplasm also undergoes a significant series of changes and that we must consider the process in its entirety before we can fully appreciate all its many aspects.

ROOTTIP CELLS IN DIVISION

The roottips of the broad bean, *Vicia faba* and the onion, *Allium cepa,* provide excellent examples of a tissue in an active state of division. The chromosomes are large and few in number (12 in *Vicia;* 16 in *Allium*), and preparations of the dividing cells are easily made.

A panoramic view of a growing roottip can be obtained from either a longitudinal section cut on a microtome or from a squashed preparation of flattened cells. The stains employed in each case are different, and the end result varies accordingly (contrast the cells of the onion with those of the broad bean in Fig. 5-1). In the cells of an onion, the *nucleoli* (one to four in number) stand out sharply in the less deeply staining nucleus (lower

Fig. 5-1. Panoramic view of sectioned and smeared roottip cells. Left, sectioned view of dividing cells in the onion root, stained with iron haemotoxylin to show chromosomes, spindle, walls and cytoplasm; the various stages of division range from interphase to telophase. Right, smeared cells from the root of the broad bean, Vicia faba; smearing disrupts the arrangement of the cells, while the Feulgen stain used in this instance is specific for chromosomes and stains no other part of the cells (X ca. 420). (Left, courtesy of General Biological Supply House, Inc., Chicago; right, courtesy Dr. T. Merz.)

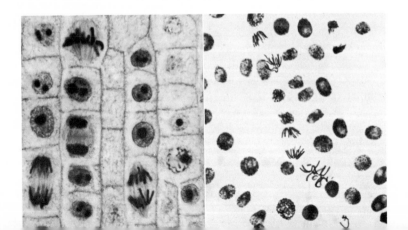

right cell in Fig. 5-3); these, however, are not evident in the broad bean cells, but this is because they are not stained rather than that they are absent.

Let us now consider the stages of nuclear division, or mitosis (Figs. 5-2 and 5-3), starting with a cell in the first stage, or *interphase*, of the division cycle. At this time the nucleus is large, in comparison with nuclei

Fig. 5-2. The progress of cell division, outlined in schematic form. As the cell prepares to divide, the chromosomes appear as distinct bodies in the nucleus, with a split along their length. The spindle appears at metaphase and separates the two chromatids of each chromosome at anaphase, after which the cell plate cuts the cell into two new cells. Karyokinesis, or mitosis, refers to the nuclear events of cell division; cytokinesis refers to the division of the cytoplasm by the cell plate.

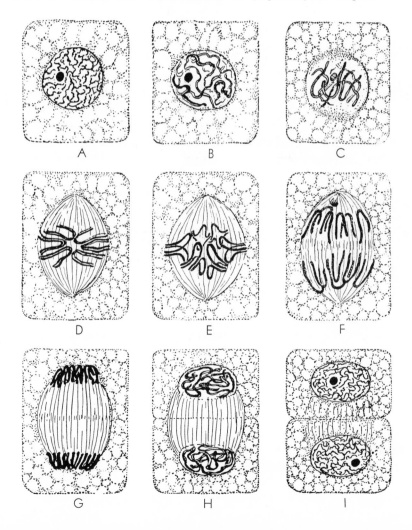

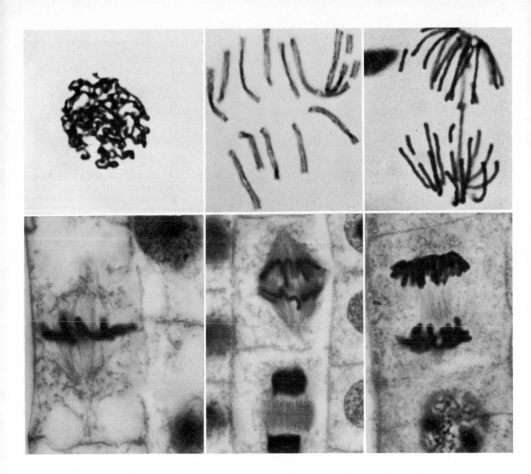

Fig. 5-3. Stages in cell division. Top row: prophase, metaphase and anaphase stages in the broad bean roottip; these cells are Feulgen stained, and only the chromosomes, which contain DNA, are evident. The gap in one arm of the two longest chromosomes is where the nucleolus was attached, and can be seen at both metaphase and anaphase stages. (Courtesy Dr. T. Merz.) Bottom row: left, metaphase; center, early anaphase and late telophase with cell plate forming across the spindle; right, late anaphase and early prophase. These cells are stained with haemotoxylin, and walls, cytoplasm, and spindle show as well as the chromosomes (X 780). (Courtesy General Biological Supply House, Inc., Chicago.)

in nondividing cell tissues. Although we do not know what mechanism stimulates a cell to divide, we do know that *nucleic acids* and *proteins,* large molecules found in every nucleus, are synthesized during interphase as a preparatory step to division. There is little definable structure except for the nucleoli and a fine network of chromatin, which means that the nucleic acids of the chromosomes are either too diffused to absorb much dye or are so hydrated that the dye is not accumulated in sufficient quantity to stain them intensely. The chromosomes, therefore, are not individually distinguishable in interphase.

The cell enters *prophase* when the chromosomes become visibly distinct as long thin threads. They are divided longitudinally into identical halves called *chromatids.* The increasing visibility of the chromosomes is probably caused by a loss of water, so that its stainable parts become more densely compacted. Equally importantly, however, the chromosomes become shorter and thicker by a process that transforms the slender chromatids into a coil, much as you might turn a thin wire into a coiled spring. As the chromatids continue to shorten throughout prophase, the coils decrease in number as they are increasing in diameter.

During prophase, the nucleoli, which are formed by particular chromosomes, are initially prominent, but they diminish in size toward the end of the stage and disappear (Fig. 5-3). The nuclear membrane also disintegrates in late prophase, contraction of the chromosomes ceases, and *metaphase* begins.

The disappearance of the nuclear membrane coincides with the appearance of a new structure in the cytoplasm, the *spindle,* which, chemically, consists of long-chain protein molecules oriented longitudinally between two *poles* (Fig. 5-4). The "fibers" of the spindle, however are really fine tubules, not just protein threads. Chemical analysis of cells has indicated that approximately 15 per cent of the cytoplasmic proteins go into

Fig. 5-4. Electron micrographs of spindles and spindle structure in sea urchin eggs. Upper, isolated spindle at low magnification (X 2,236), with the chromosomes appearing dark on the metaphase plate, a vague region across center of spindle; lower, spindle fibers (tubules) (F) attached to the chromosome (C) (X 56,250). (Courtesy Dr. R. E. Kane.)

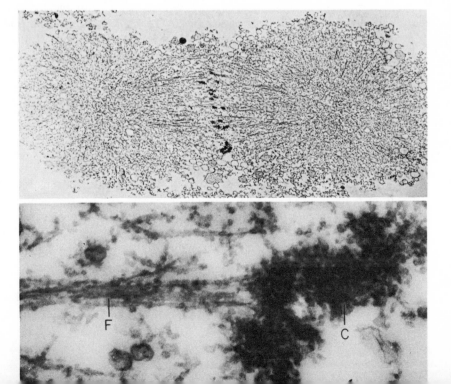

its make-up. Once the spindle is formed, the chromosomes move through the cytoplasm to it, and become fastened by their *centromeres* to a region midway between the poles called the *equator* of the spindle, a position of apparent equilibrium. The centromere of each chromosome always contacts the spindle at the equator; the arms of the chromosomes, not being so restricted, are randomly oriented. It is relatively easy to prevent the spindle from forming by putting a cell in a solution of *colchicine,* an alkaloid drug. The chromosomes then lie free in the cell, and their morphology can be easily seen (upper middle, Fig. 5-3).

The centromere is the organ of movement. Without it, a chromosome cannot orient on the spindle, and the chromatids cannot separate from each other later. The position of the centromere is visible in a chromosome during metaphase by a constriction, and since the position of the constriction is characteristic for each chromosome, the centromere divides the chromosome into two arms of varying lengths. Very few chromosomes have strictly terminal centromeres.

Anaphase follows metaphase in the mitotic cycle. The centromeres now divide so that each chromatid has its own centromere; they then move apart from each other to initiate a slow movement that will take sister chromatids to opposite poles. Termination of anaphase movement occurs when the chromosomes form a densely packed group at the two poles.

At this point, *telophase* begins. The events are essentially the reverse of those occurring in prophase: the nuclear membrane forms, the chromosomes uncoil to become slender threads again, and the nucleoli and chromocenters make their appearance. The nucleus as a whole takes on an interphase character. At the equator a new cell wall forms. Initially the *cell plate,* as it is called, is formed within the confines of the spindle, and apparently from elements of the Golgi apparatus (see Fig. 5-5), but soon it crosses to the outer walls to segment the cytoplasm into roughly equal parts. The spindle then disintegrates, cell division is completed, and two new cells are formed.

DIVISION IN ANIMAL CELLS

The cells of the whitefish (*Coregonus*) embryo illustrate very beautifully the division process and reveal the differences that distinguish animal from plant cells (Fig. 5-6). The chromosomes behave the same in both forms though they are more numerous and smaller in the whitefish cell than in those of the onion or broad bean. The most immediate difference lies in the process of spindle formation. As Fig. 5-6 reveals, the whitefish cell in prophase shows a radiating structure adjacent to the nuclear membrane. This is the *centrosome,* with astral *rays* radiating from it and with a central body, or *centriole* (not visible in Fig. 5-6), contained within it. During prophase, or even before, the centriole divides, and the halves

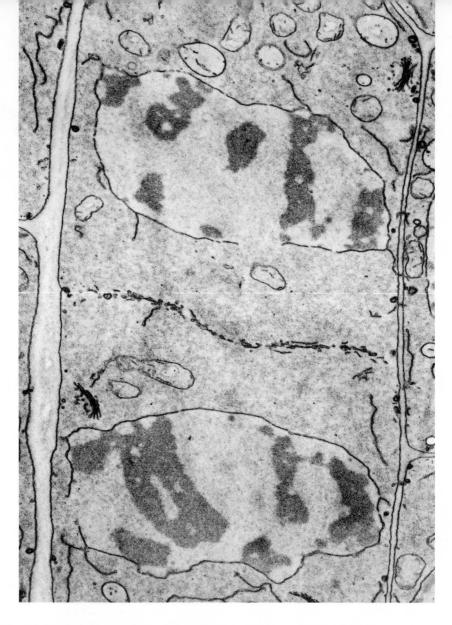

Fig. 5-5. Electron micrograph of a maize cell in late telophase, with the cell plate forming across the center. (Courtesy Dr. G. Whaley.)

migrate along the membrane until they lie opposite each other. When the nuclear membrane breaks down, they organize the cellular proteins into the spindle in such a way that the centrioles are at the poles with the spindle between them. It is not known how the centrosomes and centrioles perform this task. Astral rays also extend into the cytoplasm, but they perform no known function unless they are included in the spindle. The cycle through which the centriole proceeds during division is depicted in Fig. 5-7, the

69

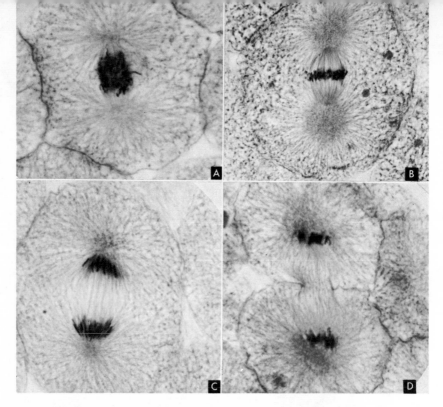

Fig. 5-6. Stages in division in the whitefish. (A) Prophase, with spindle beginning to form; (B) Metaphase; (C) Anaphase; (D) Telophase, with the furrow cutting the cell into two new daughter cells. (Copyright by General Biological Supply House, Inc., Chicago.)

Fig. 5-7. Formation of the spindle by the long centriole in the protozoan, Barbulanympha. Note that the new centrioles for the next division are already in evidence; these will lengthen between divisions to reach full size. The rounded structure is the centrosome. (From L. R. Cleveland.)

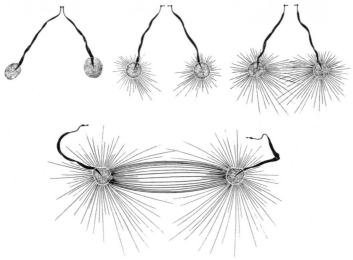

example being taken from the protozoa where the centriole is a very large structure.

The division of the whitefish mother cell into two new daughter cells is another point of difference. A process of *furrowing,* beginning at the outer edges of the cell in the vicinity of the equator, cleaves the cell in two. Plant cells, with their rigid cell walls, cannot do this, but the process of cell plate formation accomplishes the same thing.

THE SEQUENCE OF EVENTS IN CELL DIVISION

Many aspects of cell division are not explained by a simple description of the events taking place in a cell as it passes from one interphase to another. It must be apparent, however, that the cell cycle, in order to be completed, is a delicately balanced and coordinated process, with the nucleus, the cytoplasm, and their constituent parts coming in on cue to play their necessary roles. One mistake and an abnormal cell results.

Figure 5-8 diagrams the events taking place before and during cell division. The events occurring prior to prophase, although not visible under the microscope directly, are of primary importance because they prepare the cell for the more dramatic events of prophase, metaphase, anaphase, and telophase. Indeed, it now appears that a cell prepares to divide long before the actual division takes place, but whether division does occur is determined by later events; that is, some cells, such as those in nerves and muscles, may have had their division cycle permanently interrupted, and will never divide again, whereas others, as those in blood-forming tissues or roottips, will divide continuously during the life of an organism.

Fig. 5-8. Table of events taking place in preparation for, and during, cell division. (After D. Mazia.)

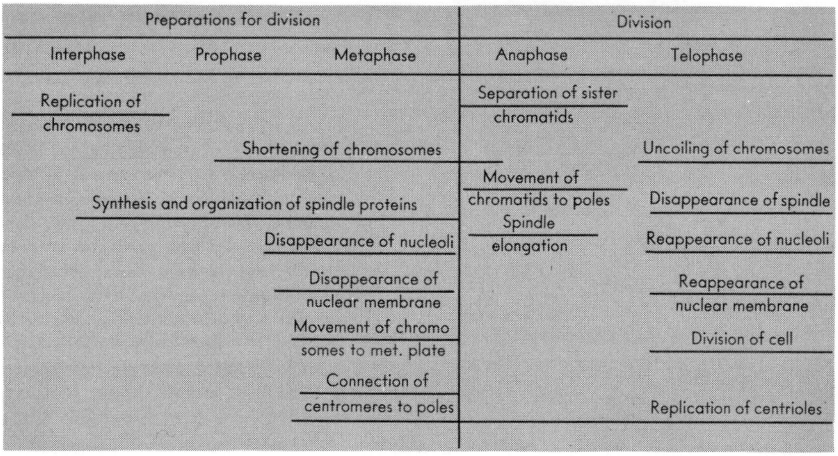

Preparations for division			Division	
Interphase	Prophase	Metaphase	Anaphase	Telophase
Replication of chromosomes			Separation of sister chromatids	
		Shortening of chromosomes		Uncoiling of chromosomes
	Synthesis and organization of spindle proteins		Movement of chromatids to poles	Disappearance of spindle
		Disappearance of nucleoli	Spindle elongation	Reappearance of nucleoli
		Disappearance of nuclear membrane		Reappearance of nuclear membrane
		Movement of chromosomes to met. plate		Division of cell
		Connection of centromeres to poles		Replication of centrioles

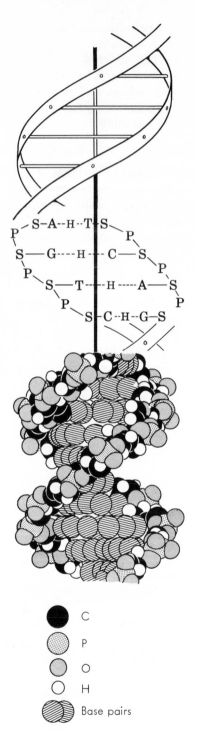

C

P

O

H

Base pairs

The first step in preparation is the division of the centrioles, an event that took place almost a whole cell cycle in advance. This is followed by the replication of the chromosome, and the synthesis of those proteins that will eventually form the spindle. Both of these events are now reasonably well understood as the result of research done in the last decade.

The replication of the chromosomes, and of the genes they contain, is related to the structure of the DNA molecule. Figure 5-9 illustrates the accepted version of this molecule. Chemical analysis reveals it to be a compound of very high molecular weight, made up of a number of smaller molecules linked together in a particular and precise manner. These molecules include a sugar, *deoxyribose, phosphoric acid,* and four bases, two of which are pyrimidines (*thymine* and *cytosine*) and two purines (*adenine* and *guanine*). The chemical structure of each base is given in Fig. 5-10, together with their mode of linkage by hydrogen atoms. The alternating sugar and phosphate arrangement forms the outside boundaries of DNA, while base pairs link the two sides together. The base pairs,

Fig. 5-9. The helix of DNA, with three different ways of representing the molecular arrangement. Top, general picture of the double helix, with the phosphate-sugar combinations making up the outside spirals and the base pairs the cross-bars. Middle, a somewhat more detailed representation: phosphate (P), sugar (S), adenine (A), thymine (T), guanine (G), cytosine (C), and hydrogen (H). Bottom, detailed structure showing how the space is filled with atoms: carbon (C), oxygen (O), hydrogen (H), phosphorus (P), and the base pairs.

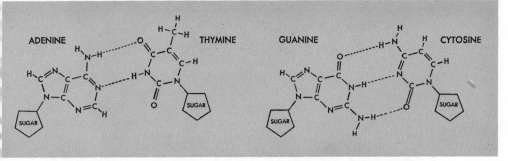

Fig. 5-10. Chemical configurations of the four bases found in the DNA molecule, arranged as base pairs. Thymine and cytosine are pyrimidines; ademine and guanine are purines.

however, are not at random, for adenine and thymine are always paired, as are guanine and cytosine. X-ray analysis of the molecular arrangement has demonstrated that DNA is not a flat structure, but rather a double helix, a sort of "spiral staircase" with alternating sugar-phosphate "bannisters" and "steps" of base pairs. This is the Watson-Crick model of DNA, so named after its discoverers.

We do not know the length of the DNA molecule in many organisms, but the single chromosome in a bacterial virus is 40 microns long, and has a molecular weight of about 40,000,000. A complete turn in the spiral occurs every 34 A, so there must be thousands of such turns in a single molecule. It is of interest in connection with replication that the molecule can uncoil as it reproduces itself. This characteristic is shown for a short fragment of DNA in Fig. 5-11, and the mode of replication is such as to give two identical molecules, or chromosomes. The amount of DNA is therefore doubled in interphase, and the daughter cells will possess the same genes, and in the same order, as did the mother cell from which they were derived. It is by this means that inheritance, embodied in the DNA molecule, is passed along from cell to cell, as well as from generation to generation.

The chromosome also contains RNA, *histones,* and a more complex protein. The histones, which are tightly bound to DNA, are synthesized at the same time, but we know little about how these four kinds of molecule are chemically associated to form a microscopically visible chromosome.

Figure 5-8 also indicates that the fibrous proteins of the spindle are synthesized, at least in part, during interphase. Chemical analysis of isolated spindles indicates a single type of protein combined with about 5% RNA. With the beginning of prophase, the spindle proteins are present in the cell, but in an unassembled form. Most of the protein appears to be of cytoplasmic rather than nuclear origin, although both parts of the cell may contribute spindle substance. Just before metaphase, the spindle proteins are oriented longitudinally between the centrioles (or the poles when no centrioles are evident), with some of the protein organized into

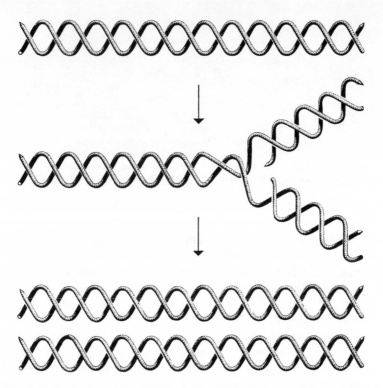

Fig. 5-11. Replication of the DNA molecule which takes place during interphase. The old helix unwinds (middle) and the two new helixes are being formed.

distinct filaments connecting centrioles and the centromeres of chromosomes. Some filaments may extend from pole to pole, or simply project into the cytoplasm as astral rays.

The organization of spindle proteins brings the centromeres of chromosomes onto the metaphase plate, a position of equilibrium. With the onset of anaphase, the fibers between centriole and centromere shorten, separating the chromatids and moving them closer to the poles. Additional separation of the chromatids is brought about by an elongation of that region of the spindle lying between them. The mechanisms involved in these two kinds of anaphase movement are not yet fully understood, however. After the separation, nuclei are formed at the poles, and the cytoplasm divides into two cells.

Figure 5-8 depicts still other events that transpire during cell division: the shortening of the chromosomes in prophase by coiling and their uncoiling at telophase, the disappearance and reappearance of nucleoli and nuclear membrane, the formation of a cell plate or a furrow to divide the cytoplasm, and the disappearance of the spindle. These, like replication and the formation of spindle proteins, are all chemical events, but although we can follow the course of events during the cell cycle, we know little of the basic biochemistry of any single one of these phenomena except the replication of DNA.*

How long does it take a cell to go through the entire process of division, and what is the time spent in each stage of cell division. We can best determine this by examining, under a phase-contrast microscope, a dividing cell while it is still alive (cells grown in tissue culture are good for this type of study). We find that the rate of cell division is characteristic of the organism in question, and that the rate can be governed very easily by varying such factors as nutrition and temperature. Let us take the human fibrocyte (a type of generalized connective cell) as an example, since it is now possible to grow these readily in tissue culture. The entire cycle of cell division takes approximately 18 hours from initiation to completion, that is, from interphase to interphase. Yet from the beginning of prophase to the end of telophase requires only about 45 minutes. The cell thus spends approximately 17 hours preparing itself for division, after which it goes through the process in a relatively explosive fashion. Other cells, and indeed other strains of fibrocytes, may take longer. To understand the process of cell division, therefore, it is quite clear that we must know what is taking place in the preparatory stages leading up to the initiation of prophase. As we have indicated, our knowledge of this process is extremely limited at the present time.

Figure 5-12 shows the division cycle of the neuroblast cells of the grasshopper embryo. The cells, which lie on the surface of the embryo, divide to form tissue that eventually becomes incorporated into the nervous system of the grasshopper at maturity. It can be seen that at 38°C the length of time for the entire process is approximately 3½ hours. A large portion of the time, in fact about half of it, is spent in prophase. Metaphase and anaphase are fairly short, but the reorganization of the nucleus takes a longer period of time. Interphase in this particular type of cell is quite short, compared to that of the human cell described above. If, however, the temperature is lowered to 26°C, the whole division cycle is lengthened to approximately 8 hours instead of 3½.

The effect of temperature on the rate of cell division has been strikingly revealed in studies of the stamen hair cells of a plant called *Tradescantia*. The hairs are long filaments consisting of a chain of individual cells; only the terminal cell goes through division. A complete division takes place in about 135 minutes if the temperature is 10°C, but at 45°C it takes only 30 minutes. As you would expect, organisms vary greatly in their time of division. Bacteria, at 37°C, will go through a division every 15 to 20

* For greater details, see D. M. Bonner and S. E. Mills, *Heredity,* 2nd ed. (Englewood Cliffs, N. J.: Prentice-Hall, 1964).

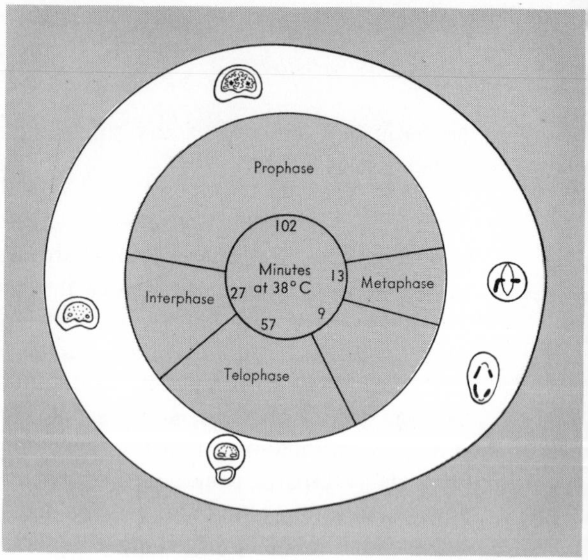

Fig. 5-12. Time sequence of cell division in certain cells of a grasshopper embryo that complete their cycle in 208 minutes at 38 C. At lower temperatures, the cycle would be correspondingly lengthened. (Redrawn from J. G. Carlson.)

minutes, whereas roottip cells generally take about 22 hours at room temperature. Some roottip cells continue to divide at 0°C, but we know little about the time span at that temperature. Warm-blooded animals show a lesser range of tolerance; cell division ceases at temperatures below 24°C or above 46°C.

THE SIGNIFICANCE OF CELL DIVISION

Cell division is, of course, part of the process of growth. Although the dance of the chromosomes, the formation of the spindle, and the formation of daughter cells are the more obvious parts of the drama, it also involves the assimilation of materials from the outside, their transformation through breakdown and synthesis into new cellular parts, and the utilization of energy. Cell enlargement also takes place. We know of no cells, except the fertilized egg and a few of its derivative cells, that simply divide from one large cell into two others of half size and again into four cells of quarter size. This is not the usual way cell division proceeds, for interspersed in the process are periods of growth; each division is a tumultuous affair, from which the cells must recover before proceeding again through the cycle.

Of great significance to growth, too, is the fact that cell division insures a continuous succession of similarly endowed cells. Chaos would result if only a random array of cells of varying qualities and capacities were to reproduce themselves; organized growth must proceed from cells of similar nature that can subsequently be molded according to the demands of the species. The species could not otherwise persist. We mentioned earlier that the chromosome is an intricate fabric composed of nucleic acids and proteins. Since the nucleus is the control center of the cell, and since the nucleus contains little else but chromosomes, the chromosomes must be the regulators of cellular metabolism and the structural characteristics of the cell. Therefore, if two cells are to behave similarly they must have the same amount and type of nucleic acids and proteins. The longitudinal duplication of the chromosomes into identical chromatids and their segregation to the poles at anaphase must be exact to the minutest degree; the kind of cell division described provides the mechanism needed. From the time a particular species was formed, this process of cell division has gone on with an exactitude that almost defies the imagination. Accidents and variations do occur, and indeed they must if evolution is to take place, but they are relatively few in number.

Let us ask another question. Why is it that cells divide? Or, in reverse, why is it that reproducing cells stop dividing? If we take a cell such as an ameba, we can observe that it reaches a certain size and then divides. If we starve it, it will shrink and stop dividing. It would appear, therefore, that cell division is an attempt to keep a fairly constant ratio between the amount of the nucleus and the amount of the cytoplasm. This view makes sense, for if the nucleus governs the activities of the cell, it can exercise efficient control over only a certain amount of cytoplasmic material. If the cytoplasm should exceed a certain amount, the power of the nucleus over it becomes less and less. For example, an ameba can be prevented from dividing by cutting off each day bits of the growing cytoplasm, thus keeping the ratio of cytoplasm to nucleus constant. Yet the problem isn't quite so simple as it might appear. If the nucleus of an actively dividing ameba is inserted into an ameba that is in a quiescent state (this can be done with a micropipette without damaging either the nucleus or the cytoplasm), nothing happens unless both the nucleus and the cytoplasm are ready for cell division to occur. What we mean by a state of maturity is still somewhat uncertain, but obviously both these parts must be prepared for division before the process of cell division can go on in any organized fashion.

Looked at in another way, cell division is an act of survival. Cells eventually die if they do not divide, just as multicellular organisms must die if they possess no way of subdividing their bodies to produce new organisms. Division, however, accompanied by the usual growth that follows division, brings fresh substance into the cell, effectively preventing aging and giving to the cell a potential immortality. In a multicellular organism, on the other hand, cell division provides added cells, among which a division of labor can take place. Viewed in this manner, cell division is therefore, a first step towards cell differentiation. But this is the antithesis of survival, because differentiation is also a first step toward eventual death since differentiated cells lose their capacity to divide. The significance of cell division, then, depends not only on the phenomenon itself, but also on the kind of cell that is dividing and the consequences of division to an organism.

Meiosis and Sexual Reproduction

The continuation of any species, man or ameba, oak tree or bacteria, depends on an unending succession of individuals. No organism is immortal, so its population must reproduce if it is to escape extinction. In unicellular organisms such as the ameba, cell division serves this function; it is a reproductive device that leads to the continued formation of new individuals. And, since mitosis is a mechanism that maintains a constant chromosome number, all offspring arising through mitosis have the same number of chromosomes as the original ameba.

The ameba, however, like many unicellular and some multicellular organisms, is asexual; it does not produce sexual cells—*eggs* and *sperm*. But other unicellular and most multicellular organisms reproduce by sexual means; sometime during their life cycle they produce *gametes* (a general term applied to any type of sexual cell) which unite in pairs to form a single new cell called a *zygote*. From this cell a new individual develops. The union of gametes is called *fertilization* or *syngamy*.

It is important to recognize that when two gametes unite

through fertilization, the principal event is the fusion of gametic nuclei. Let us consider what this means in terms of chromosome number. The cells of the human being, for example, contain 46 chromosomes (Fig. 6-1). If we assume for the moment that mitosis is the only type of nuclear division, the human egg and sperm would each contain 46 chromosomes, since they arise by division from the original zygote. The zygote formed by their union would then contain 92 chromosomes, and so, too, would the eggs and sperm produced by the individual developing from the new zygote. The individuals of the next generation would possess 184 chromosomes, and by the end of the tenth generation each individual would have cells containing 23,332 chromosomes.

Obviously, this would be a ridiculous state of affairs. The illustration merely emphasizes that, in a sexually breeding population, the increase in chromosome number resulting from fertilization cannot go on indefinitely. Sometime during the life cycle of an individual some compensatory

Fig. 6-1. The chromosomes of a normal human male, with the chromosomes arranged in homologous pairs and numbered according to size. The male has an XY sex-determining system; the small Y chromosome is indicated at the bottom right, while the X, which is difficult to identify positively, is one of those in the second row. A female would have an XX chromosomal composition; the Y would be absent, and another X would replace it. (Courtesy Dr. Barbara Migeon.)

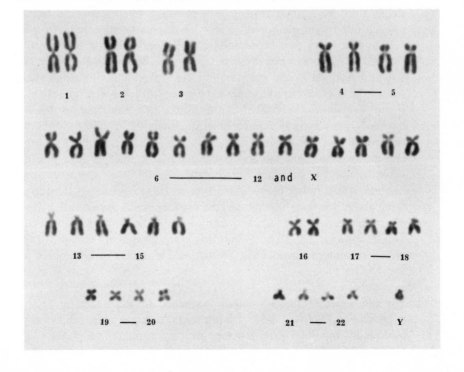

mechanism must reduce this number, for we know that the cells of individuals belonging to the same species have a striking constancy of chromosome number. Thus, normal human cells have 46 chromosomes, those of maize has 20, of the mouse 40, of the rat 42, and so forth. The lowest number known is 2, found in a round worm, whereas, some plants and animals have numbers as high as several hundred. This numerical constancy for each species is repeated generation after generation. The gametes, therefore, must have half the number of chromosomes found in the zygote and in the other cells of the body (since the latter arise from the zygote by mitosis). The reduction in number of chromosomes is accomplished by a special type of cell division called *meiosis,* which in its barest essentials consists of *two nuclear divisions but only one division of chromosomes.*

Before considering the details of meiosis, and the features that distinguish this type of cell division from mitosis, we need to recognize certain terms that conveniently describe chromosomal states. The chromosomes in the nuclei of gametes are called, variously, the *reduced, gametic, haploid,* or *n* number, while those in the zygote and all cells derived from it by mitosis are termed the *unreduced, zygotic, diploid,* or *2n* number. Thus, a human egg, prior to fertilization, possesses 23 chromosomes, in contrast to the 46 in the zygote. Furthermore, the 46 chromosomes are not all individually different; they exist as 23 pairs, the members of each pair being similar in shape, size, and genetic content. The members of each pair are *homologous* to each other, and *nonhomologous* with respect to the other chromosomes. In a zygote every pair of homologous chromosomes, or *homologues,* thus consists of one member contributed by the sperm and one by the egg.

One execption to the comparability of paired homologues in shape and size is the pair of chromosomes concerned with the determination of sex. Figure 6-1 shows this pair of chromosomes in a human male; the X chromosome is involved in female determination, the Y chromosome in male determination. The human female is XX, and consequently her paired chromosomes are similar and homologous; the male is XY, and the two chromosomes are essentially nonhomologous.

Meiosis is a rather complicated type of cell division, yet the remarkable thing about it is that, like mitosis, the nuclear events are essentially the same wherever encountered. Consequently a single account of it applies equally well to a fungus, an insect, a flowering plant, or a man. Except for the type of cell resulting from meiosis, the process is similar in both sexes as well.

THE STAGES OF MEIOSIS

We can separate meiosis into a sequence of steps similar to those in mitosis (Figs. 6-2 and 6-3). Prophase, however, is longer in duration and profoundly modified in character, and five separate prophase stages are recognizable.

Fig. 6-2. Diagrammatic representation of the states of division in meiosis I and II. For simplification, only one pair of homologues is included. (M. M. Rhoades, Journal of Heredity, **41. 1950, 59–67.)**

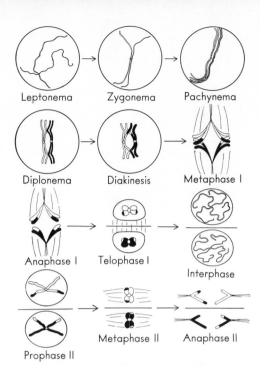

Leptonema → Zygonema → Pachynema

Diplonema → Diakinesis → Metaphase I

Anaphase I → Telophase I → Interphase

Prophase II → Metaphase II → Anaphase II

THE STAGES OF MEIOSIS

Fig. 6-3. Stages of meiosis in Trillium. (A) zygotene; (B) pachytene; (C) early diplotene; (D) late diplotene; (E) diakinesis; (F) metaphase I; (G) late anaphase I; (H) metaphase II (prophase II is absent in this plant); (I) anaphase II; (J) quartet stage, with four microspores. (Courtesy Dr. A. H. Sparrow.)

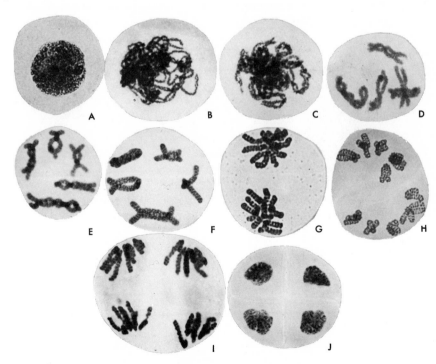

The *leptotene* stage initiates meiosis. Meiotic cells and their nuclei are generally larger than those of the surrounding tissues. The chromosomes, present in the diploid number, are thinner and longer than in mitosis, and are therefore difficult to distinguish individually. Leptotene chromosomes, however, differ from those in ordinary mitotic prophase in two ways: (1) they *appear* to be longitudinally single rather than double, although the timing of DNA synthesis suggests that they may in fact be double, and (2) their structure is more definite, with a series of dense granules, or *chromomeres,* occurring at irregular intervals along their length. The chromomeres of any given organism are characteristic in number, size, and position, and consequently can be used as landmarks to identify particular chromosomes. It has been estimated that in the garden lily, for example, there are about 2000 chromomeres in the entire set of 24 chromosomes, although in the plant, *Luzula,* the number is far fewer (Fig. 6-4).

Movement of the chromosomes initiates the *zygotene* stage, and this

Fig. 6-4. Meiotic prophase (pachytene stage) in the wood rush, Luzula, showing the numerous chromomeres along the paired homologues, and the nucleolus with its attached chromosomes. (Courtesy Dr. S. Brown.)

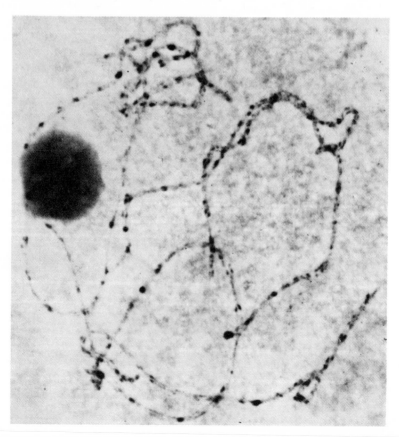

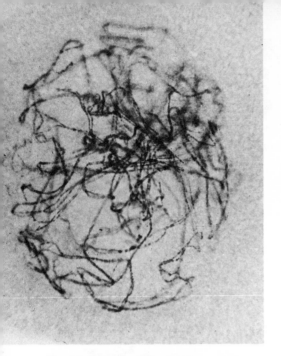

Fig. 6-5. Zygotene stage of meiosis in the regal lily, Lilium regale. **In the lower right hand corner, both paired and unpaired regions of the homologues are visible. (Courtesy Dr. J. MacLeish.)**

movement results from an attracting force that brings together homologous chromosomes. The pairing of homologues, known as *synapsis,* begins at one or more points along the length of the chromosomes and then proceeds, much as a zipper would, to unite the homologues along their entire length. This is an exact, not a random, process, for the chromomeres in one homologue synapse exactly with their counterparts in the other (Fig. 6-5). When synapsis is complete, the nucleus will appear as if only the haploid number of chromosomes is present. Each, however, is a pair of homologous chromosomes, and these are referred to as *bivalents.*

If the zygotene stage is the period of active synapsis, the next, or *pachytene,* stage is the stable period. The paired chromosomes of each bivalent are easily seen (Fig. 6-4), and since the chromosomes have shortened and thickened, they are more readily distinguished one from the other. The chromomeres and the attachment of the nucleolus to a particular chromosome may be visible with high magnification (Figs. 6-4 and 6-6A).

The pachytene stage ends when the synaptic forces of attraction lapse and the homologous chromosomes separate from each other. This is the *diplotene* stage, and as Fig. 6-6B indicates, each chromosome now consists of two chromatids. The bivalent, therefore, is composed of four chromatids. Longitudinal division of each chromosome, except in the region of the centromere, took place prior to this stage, but did not become obviously evident until the attraction between homologues ceased.

Separation of the homologues, however, is not complete. At one or more points along their length, contact is retained by means of *chiasmata* (singular, *chiasma*). Each chiasma results from an exchange of chromatids between the two homologues; we shall discuss later in this chapter the significance of this phenomenon as it relates to heredity.

When only one chiasma has formed, the bivalent in the diplotene stage appears as a cross (Fig. 6-6B). If two are formed, the bivalent is generally ring-shaped; if three or more form, the homologues assume a looped appearance. In different cells, the number and approximate positions of the

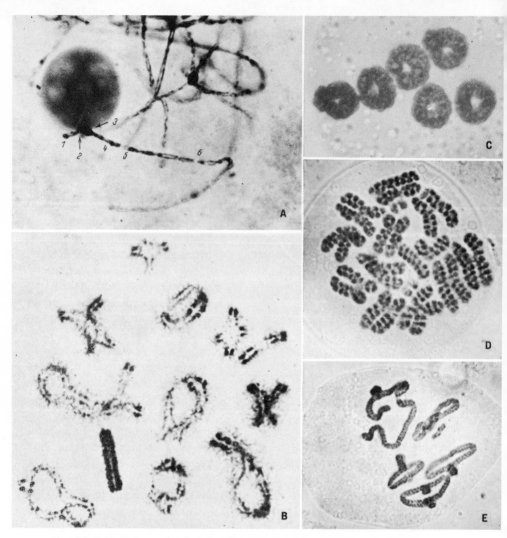

Fig. 6-6. Several stages of meiosis in different organisms. (A) Pachytene in maize, showing chromosome 6 and its attached nucleolus; the double nature of the chromosomes is evident, and the numbers indicate identifiable regions (B. McClintock, Zeitschr. Zelif. u. Mikr. Anat. 21: 294–328, 1934). (B) Diplotene stage in a spermatocyte of a grasshopper, Schistocerca gregaria; the unpaired X-chromosome is seen as a deeply stained rod, whereas chiasmata are visible in the paired homologues (J. J. Tijo and A. Levan, Ana. Est. Exp. Aula Dei 3, 2:225–228, 1954). (C) Metaphase I in Tradescantia, with most of the chiasmata at terminal positions. (D) Flattened anaphase I, showing the coiled structure of the chromosomes in Tradescantia. (E) Metaphase I in Tradescantia, with the chiasmata an interstitial positions; compare with (C).

chiasmata vary, even for the same bivalent, but, as a rule, long chromosomes have more chiasmata than short ones, although even the shortest seem to be able to form at least one chiasma.

The next prophase stage is called *diakinesis,* but the distinction between it and the diplotene stage is not a sharp one. During diakinesis the nucleolus becomes detached from its special bivalent and disappears, and the bivalents become considerably more contracted (Fig. 6-3E). Also, as contraction proceeds, the chiasmata tend to lose their original position and move towards the ends of the chromosomes.

We have mentioned that the chromosomes shorten as they progress from the leptotene stage onward through prophase. This is accomplished by the development of a series of coils, which gradually decrease in number as their diameters increase. The process is no different from the shortening of chromosomes in mitosis; the coils here, however, are more easily observed, particularly when the cells have been pretreated with ammonia vapors or dilute cyanide solution before staining. Figure 6-6D illustrates the coils as they appear in the spiderwort, *Tradescantia.*

The breakdown of the nuclear membrane and the appearance of the spindle terminate prophase and initiate the *first metaphase of meiosis* (Figs. 6-6C and E). The bivalents then orient themselves on the spindle, but instead of all centromeres being on the equatorial plate, as in mitosis, each bivalent is so located that its centromeres lie on either side of, and equidistant from, the plate. This seems to be a position of equilibrium.

The *first anaphase* of meiosis begins with the movement of the chromosomes to the poles (Fig. 6-3G). The two centromeres of each bivalent remain undivided, and their movement to the opposite poles of the spindle causes the remaining chiasmata to slip off and free the homologues from each other. When movement ceases, a reduced, or haploid, number of chromosomes will be located at each pole. Unlike mitotic anaphase, in which the chromosomes appear longitudinally single, each chromosome now consists of two distinctly separated chromatids united only at their centromeres. The nucleus then forms, the chromosomes uncoil, and the meiotic cell is bisected by a membrane wall. This is the *first telophase of meiosis.*

After an interphase which, depending on the species involved, may be short or long—it may even be absent altogether—the chromosomes in each of the two haploid cells enter the *second meiotic division* (Fig. 6-3). If an interphase is absent, the chromosomes pass directly from the first telophase to the *second prophase* without any change in appearance. If an interphase is present, a nuclear membrane forms in telophase, the chromosomes uncoil, and a somewhat more prolonged second prophase is found. But, whatever the case, the chromosomes reaching the *second metaphase* are essentially unchanged from what they were in the previous anaphase; i.e., *no chromosomal reproduction occurs during interphase,* and the centromere of each chromosome remains undivided. A spindle forms in each of the two cells, and, at the *second anaphase,* the centromeres divide and the chromosomes move to the poles. The nuclei are reorganized during the *second telophase*, giving four haploid nuclei that become segregated into individual cells by segmentation of the cytoplasm.

Looking back over the events of meiosis, we find that the chromosomes remained unchanged in longitudinal structure from the diplotene stage to the end of the second meiotic division. The reproduction of each chromosome occurred during pachytene or earlier, but this was followed by two divisions; in the first the homologues separated from each other to reduce chromosome number, an event made possible because synapsis joined them; in the second the two chromatids of each chromosome separated.

At this point you may well ask why the reduction in chromosome number could not be accomplished just as efficiently with a single division instead of two. No logical answer can be given, but where only a single meiotic division is found, as happens during sperm formation in the normally haploid male honey bee, and where a reduction in chromosome number is not a necessary feature in the life cycle, it is essentially like the second rather than the first division. In organisms that have a diploid chromosome number, the two divisions make more sense, particularly when considered from the point of view of heredity.

THE PRODUCTS OF MEIOSIS

In the animal kingdom, meiosis leads to the formation of sexual gametes, the egg and sperm usually being the only cells carrying a haploid complement of chromosomes. In the plant kingdom, however, meiosis can occur at various times during the life cycle, and the haploid products may be sexual gametes or asexual spores, depending on the particular group of plants being studied. Since the plant life cycles are covered in another volume in this series,* we shall consider here only the products of vertebrate meiosis, that is, the egg and the sperm.

Figure 6-7 is a section through a mammalian ovary, with *oocytes,* or immature eggs, in various stages of development from their origin in the *germinal epithelium,* the outermost layer of cells, to eventual release prior to fertilization. The oocytes are formed early in life and do not increase in number thereafter; in birds and mammals, including man, the female enters reproductive life with the ovaries provided with a finite number of oocytes. In human beings, this number is reached by the fifth or sixth month of fetal life, and by birth, the oocytes have entered meiosis and have reached the diplotene stage. Diplonema can therefore persist for a period of 12 to 50 years, the approximate times when the first and last eggs are shed. During the remainder of the period, the growth of the oocytes is essentially a matter of enlargement and the storage of nutrients. The time

* H. C. Bold, *The Plant Kingdom,* 2nd ed. (Englewood Cliffs, N. J.: Prentice-Hall, 1964).

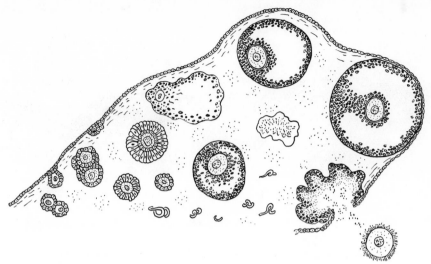

Fig. 6-7. Section of mammalian ovary, showing the progressive development of the oocytes as they arise from the germinal epithelium, increase in size, sink into the interior of the ovary wall, and finally escape to the outside by rupture of the wall of the Graafian follicle.

sequence in other mammals varies according to the length of their reproductive span, but the principle remains the same.

Initially, the *primary oocytes* lie close to the germinal epithelium, but later they increase in size and sink into the interior of the ovary where they become surrounded by *follicle cells,* which probably have both a protective and a nutritive function. The whole structure is known as a *Graafian follicle.* During this process of enlargement and encapsulation, the oocyte is building up reserve food material, the yolk. This food, which may be protein or fat, in mammals is generally distributed throughout the cytoplasm as yolk spheres or granules. In the frog, however, the yolk so completely fills the cell that the cytoplasm is restricted to a small fraction of the cell surrounding the nucleus; the well-known yolk in the hen's egg is also enormous compared to the amount of cytoplasm.

Eventually, the Graafian follicle ruptures and the egg, or ovum, is released from the ovary, and passes into the *oviduct* where it can be fertilized by a sperm. By this time, however, meiosis has been resumed, the sperm being the initiating agent. Only a *single* functional cell results, however. The other three cells, or *polar bodies,* are cast off and will degenerate, *but the process has effectively reduced the chromosome number without depriving the egg of the cytoplasm and yolk the embryo will need when it begins to develop.*

The first meiotic division in the primary oocyte takes place close to the cell membrane, and the outermost nucleus, together with a small amount of cytoplasm, is pinched off as a polar body (Fig. 6-8). The second meiotic division results in the pinching off of a second polar body; the first polar body, meanwhile, has also undergone a second meiotic divi-

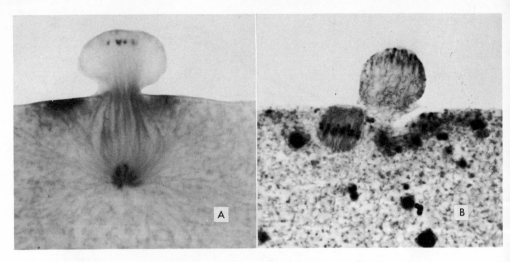

Fig. 6-8. Polar body formation in the egg of the whitefish, Coregonus. (A) Anaphase of the first meiotic division, with the first polar body being pinched off. (B) Metaphase of the second meiotic division, which will lead to the pinching off of a second polar body. In the meantime, the first polar body may also divide to give a total of three polar bodies. (Copyright by General Biological Supply House, Inc., Chicago.)

sion, thus giving a total of three polar bodies. The haploid nucleus remaining in the egg is now known as the *female pronucleus*. It sinks into the center of the cytoplasm and is ready for union with a similar haploid nucleus brought in by the sperm during fertilization.

The sperm are produced in the *semeniferous tubules* of the testes; these convoluted tubes make up 90 per cent of the male gonadal tissue. Each tube is lined with germinal *epithelium* and *Sertoli* cells (Fig. 6-9);

Fig. 6-9. Arrangements of cells and the order of progression of spermatogenesis in the semeniferous tubule: (A) basement membrane; (B) Sertoli cells; (C) spermatogonial cells, which by mitosis give rise to the primary spermatocytes (D); (E) secondary spermatocytes; (F) spermatids; (G) mature sperm.

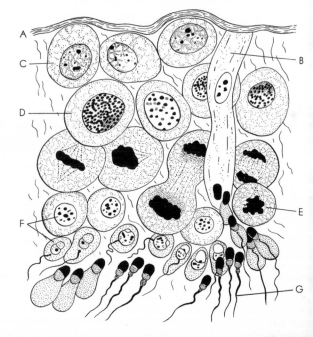

the former give rise to the germ cells, whereas the later, called "sperm mother cells," are thought to assist the newly formed sperm to undergo a ripening process.

The germinal epithelium contains *spermatogonia,* cells that continue to increase their number by mitotic division until senility sets in. These mature into *primary spermatocytes,* which undergo a first meiotic division to produce *secondary spermatocytes;* the latter pass through a second meiotic division, giving four cells called *spermatids.* These become motile sperm by a remarkable transformation of the entire cell.

The mature sperm consists essentially of a head and a tail. The head is a highly compacted nucleus, capped by a structure known as the *acrosome* (Fig. 6-10). It is derived from the Golgi materials of the spermatid, and apparently functions as a device for penetrating the egg during fertilization. Just back of the compacted nucleus is the *middle piece,* formed by an aggregation of the mitochrondria. It develops as a sheath around the *filament,* or tail, and provides the tail with energy for locomotion. The filament, in turn, has developed as the result of a tremendous elongation of one of the centrioles; the other centriole remains just beneath

Fig. 6-10. Transformation of the Golgi complex (left) into the acrosome (right) during the process of spermiogenesis in the house cricket, Acheta domestica. **The paired membranes of the Golgi complex are regularly spaced, although several vacuoles are enclosed by the membranes. The sperm head at the right shows the dark, solid nucleus capped by the acrosome; the cone-shaped acrosome is formed by the Golgi complex, but the membranes of the Golgi complex are eventually sloughed off and do not become part of the acrosome. (Courtesy Dr. J. Kaye.)**

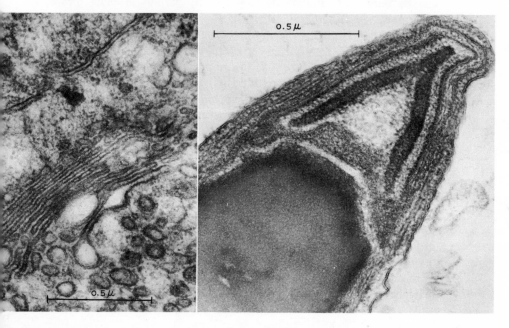

the nucleus, and at the time of fertilization enters the egg along with the male nucleus. Virtually no cytoplasm except particulate structures is used to form the mature sperm.

Each spermatid, therefore, has been transformed from a rather undifferentiated cell into a highly specialized cell capable of reaching the egg under its own power, and of penetrating it once it has made contact.

FERTILIZATION

The mature egg and sperm must unite with each other within a limited period of time, for neither has an indefinite life span. The critical period may be a few minutes, or it may be spread over several hours or days. In mammals, fertilization can occur periodically as the egg leaves the ovary and passes down the *oviduct* on its way to the *uterus*. Insects, however, mate only once, and sperm are stored in the female and used throughout the entire egg-laying period; in the honey bee, for example, this period may last a year or more. It is now possible to store mammalian sperm for an indefinite period by freezing them, and by means of *artificial insemination* the sperm of a single sire may be used to fertilize the eggs of many females; this practice has been widely used in animal breeding programs, thus passing on the superior qualities of one sire to many offspring.

The essential process of fertilization is the union of male and female pronuclei, but the sperm also functions as an activating agent. That is, nature has insured against the egg's beginning embryonic development alone; if it did, haploid embryos would result and life cycles would be hopelessly complicated. Unfertilized eggs of mammals and other related vertebrates can be induced to initiate development by various artificial means, but this rarely occurs naturally.

Fertilization is also a specific process in that the sperm of one species will not, as a rule, fertilize the egg of another species. It now appears that several chemicals are present to insure proper fertilization and to prevent the penetration of foreign sperm. The egg produces a protein substance called *fertilizin* which reacts with an *antifertilizin* on the surface of the sperm; fertilizin may act to attract sperm of its own kind, but once the two substances interact, the sperm becomes firmly attached to the egg membrane, and is then drawn into the interior of the egg. Other sperm are barred from entry by the changes that then take place in the *vitelline membrane* of the egg, an outer coating found on most eggs.

Only the nucleus and one centriole of the sperm enter the egg. The former fuses with the female pronucleus, the latter divides and begins formation of the first division spindle. In summary, therefore, the entry of the sperm into an egg contributes (1) a stimulus to development, (2) a set of haploid chromosomes, which is the paternal hereditary contribution to the newly formed zygote, and (3) a centriole, which is involved in the machinery of cell division.

GENETIC SIGNIFICANCE OF MEIOSIS

We have presented meiosis as a logical and necessary part of the life cycle of a sexually reproducing organism, i.e., it is the opposite of fertilization as regards the number of chromosomes. So far as heredity is concerned, we need to clarify two additional implications.

Figure 6-11 illustrates the segregation of chromosomes, with the paternal chromosomes indicated in black, the maternal ones in white. Each bivalent at the first meiotic metaphase would, of course, consist of two homologues, one from each parent. The orientation of all bivalents on the spindle is entirely random, so segregation at anaphase leads to a random distribution of chromosomes. The haploid cells resulting would therefore contain a mixture of paternal and maternal chromosomes. When 4 pairs of chromosomes are involved, 16 different combinations of 4 are possible. The number possible can be readily determined by calculating the value of 2^n, when n equals the number of pairs of chromosomes. In man, who has 23 pairs, the number of possible gametic chromosome combinations is 2^{23}, or 8,388,608. The chance of any single sperm or egg containing only paternal or maternal chromosomes is, therefore, negligible.

The distribution of paternal and maternal chromatin to their offspring through gametes is further complicated by the process of chiasma formation. As we pointed out before, a chiasma results from an exchange

Fig. 6-11. Diagram to represent the random segregation of paternal (black) and maternal (white) chromosomes during meiosis. Crossing over and linkage are not indicated.

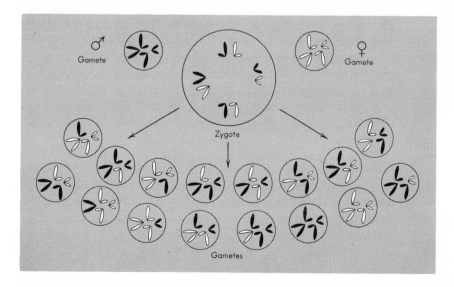

between chromatids in the two homologues. One of these is from a maternal chromosome, the other from a paternal chromosome. If we further consider that the chromosome consists of a number of genes strung along its length, and that the genes in one homologue may be slighty different for those in the other as the result of mutations, a situation such as that illustrated in Fig. 6-12 can be envisaged.

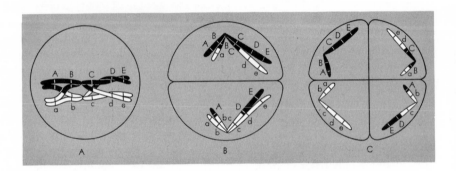

Fig. 6-12. The genetic consequences of crossing over. (A) A bivalent, consisting of paternal (black) and a maternal (white) homologue, has formed, and crossing over has taken place between genes A and B, and C and D. (B) At anaphase the two chromatids in each segregating chromosome are no longer alike genetically. (C) The chromatids are now separated and two of them have a different genetic composition, while the other two remain as before.

The genes in the paternal (black) chromosome are designated by capital letters from *A* to *E,* those in the maternal (white) one from *a* to *e.* Remember, however, that any single chromosome may have hundreds of different genes along its length. Chiasmata have formed as the result of exchanges between *A* and *B,* and between *C* and *D.* (In genetic terminology, an exchange of chromatids is called *crossing over,* and the genes *A* to *E* and *a* to *e* would constitute *linkage groups.*) The actual mechanism responsible for chiasma formation is not known for certain, but it seems clear that it occurs before the diplotene stage when the chromosomes have a clearly demonstrable double longitudinal structure. The important thing, however, is that chiasma formation breaks up linkage groups, and therefore alters the set of genes the chromosome possessed before entering meiosis. Since the chromatids eventually are distributed to the four haploid cells, it is clear that each gamete is genetically different from the others.

We see, therefore, that both the random segregation of paternal and maternal chromosomes and the breaking up of linkage groups through chiasma formation insure that the haploid cells resulting from meiosis will have a variable combination of genes. Since these cells contribute through fertilization to the next generation, the individuals of that generation must exhibit a comparable genetic variation. It is this inherited variability which natural selection acts on to bring about the evolution of organisms. Sexual reproduction, with its complementary phenomena of fertilization and meiosis, is a means not only for the production of new individuals, but of new individuals *that vary among themselves.* In this sense meiosis differs greatly from mitosis, which, in its production of similarly endowed cells, is a conservative process of reproduction.

The Cell
in Development

CHAPTER SEVEN

In the past few chapters, we have casually mentioned that organisms "develop" from a fertilized egg into a plant or animal of adult proportions. Each of us knows in a general way what is meant by development: it is a continuous and gradual process that takes time in order to be fully realized, is generally accompanied by an increase in size and weight, involves the appearance of new features and new functions, and eventually slows down when mature dimensions are reached. Man, for example, develops from the fertilized egg stage through prenatal life, childhood, adolescence, sexual maturity, physical maturity, middle age, senility, and death. Development is, of course, one of the most prominent features in the early life of an organism, but the formation of new blood cells, gametes, and wound tissue, which may take place up to death at an advanced age, are also aspects of development. So, too, are those processes we associate with aging, for example, excess formation of collagen in the extracellular spaces and the calcification of joints. These are normal processes of development continuing beyond the point of a functional and developmental optimum. These terms we have used, however, are only broadly descriptive. They tell us very little about the mechanism of development as a biological phenomenon. For that, we must approach development from the cellular level, since the cell remains the building block of life. And we must ask how the potentialities of the fertilized egg, which reside as coded information in the egg's DNA and in the organization of its cytoplasm, can become the fully realized features of a perfectly formed organism, with each organ being the right size, in its allotted place, and equipped with the cells needed to perform properly.

The problem of development in its entirety is an immense and complicated one, and includes many of the important unsolved questions of biology. Here we wish only to consider the major aspects of development, i.e., *growth, differentiation,* and *integration,* and the role of the cell in each of them.

GROWTH

Growth is defined as an increase in mass. This increase can result from an enlargement of cells, but more often it is caused by an increase in the number of cells through mitotic divisions. Growth, then, is essentially a process of replication: the original cell takes from its environment the raw materials it needs and converts them into more substance and more cells like itself. Let us consider the human egg. It weighs about one-millionth of a gram, and the sperm, at fertilization, adds to it only another five-billionths of a gram. At birth, however, a child will weigh around 7 pounds, or 3200 grams, which is an increase of about one billion times during a nine-month period. A newborn child is obviously not simply a mass of cells of comparable size and character to the original cell; if it were, it would just be a ball of cells devoid of human qualities. Nor has its growth rate been uniform throughout its prenatal life. Other processes must act to mold cells into shape, as a potter or a sculptor molds his clay, and to stamp them with character.

One of these processes is the *relative rate of growth.* This rate determines form, which is another way of saying that some parts of the body grow at a faster or slower rate than others, and that in development some features come into existence early, and others late. Figure 7-1 shows how the growth rate in the human being alters the relative proportions of bodily parts to one another. The head and neck increase in size rapidly, the arms grow faster at an earlier stage than do the legs, whereas the trunk progresses at a more or less steady rate until maturity.

Growth, therefore, is not just the multiplication of cells; it is a complicated pattern of multiplication, with different centers of growth being active at different times and at different rates of development. These centers are coordinated so as to produce an unfolding of form, and it is

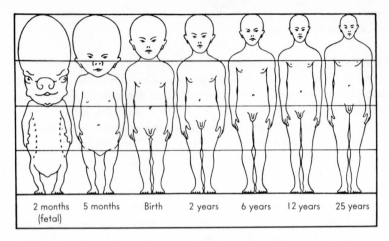

| 2 months (fetal) | 5 months | Birth | 2 years | 6 years | 12 years | 25 years |

Fig. 7-1. Changes in the form and proportion of the human body during fetal and postnatal life. (From H. B. Glass, Genes and the Man. New York: Teachers College, Columbia Univ., Bureau of Publications, 1943, after Morris.)

form as well as function, of course, that distinguishes one human being from another, men from other animals, and an orchid, for example, from a lily.

DIFFERENTIATION

It is *differentiation,* however, that stamps each cell with its own uniqueness of structure and function. A generalized cell is transformed by a process of progressive change into a specialized one, and variation is thereby introduced into a functioning organism. In man, for example, growing cells are transformed into the myriad of different cells that make up the human body: cells of the nervous, muscular, digestive, excretory, circulatory, and respiratory systems.

Differentiation is a phenomenon that has no counterpart in the nonliving world, and what little information about it we have has been derived from observations of living systems. This process is creative in the sense that life is creative, for out of the general features common to all cells arise structures and functions that are peculiar to specialized cells. Specialization can be seen in Fig. 7-2, which illustrates the origin and progressive differentiation of a special cell type, in this case, the *melanocytes* that form pigment in the human skin. Differentiation, therefore, is to development what mutation is to biological inheritance, and what imagination is to human endeavor; it provides variety.

Let us examine the process of melanocyte formation in detail since it represents an excellent example of differentiation within the cell. The melanocytes have their origin as melanoblasts in a region of the embryo called the *neural crest,* from which they migrate to the outer (*epidermis*) or inner (*dermis*) layers of the skin. As they migrate, they alter their shape, as Fig. 7-2 indicates, and they also begin to form small granules, *melanosomes,* within which the pigment *melanin* is bound.

Fig. 7-2. The origin and course of differentiation of melanin-producing cells in the human being. Top, the melanoblasts have their origin during the fetal stage in an area called the neural crest, from which they migrate and differentiate. Their ultimate fate depends on whether they end up in the dermis or the epidermis; if in the former, they cease producing melanin at birth except in special circumstances, but if in the epidermis, they continue to produce melanin until death. Below, five cells, showing the series of changes that are undergone from the round melanoblast (left) to the highly differentiated melanocyte (far right). (Courtesy Dr. A. A. Zimmermann from A. A. Zimmermann and S. W. Becker, Jr., Illinois Monographs in Medical Sciences, **VI, 1939, 1–39.**)

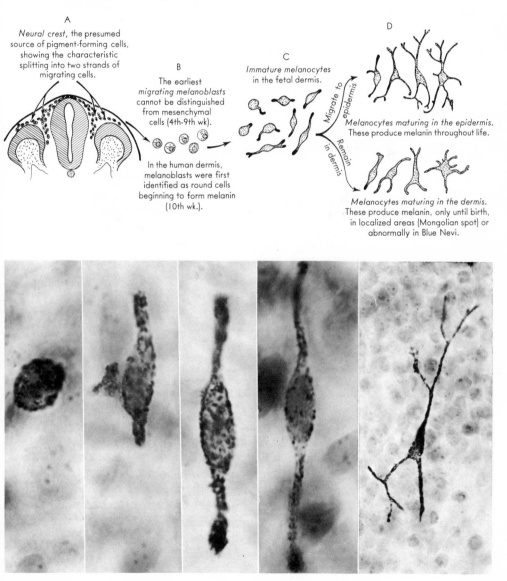

A

Neural crest, the presumed source of pigment-forming cells, showing the characteristic splitting into two strands of migrating cells.

B

The earliest *migrating melanoblasts* cannot be distinguished from mesenchymal cells (4th-9th wk).

In the human dermis, melanoblasts were first identified as round cells beginning to form melanin (10th wk.).

C

Immature melanocytes in the fetal dermis.

Migrate to epidermis

Remain in dermis

D

Melanocytes maturing in the epidermis. These produce melanin throughout life.

Melanocytes maturing in the dermis. These produce melanin, only until birth, in localized areas (Mongolian spot) or abnormally in Blue Nevi.

Figure 7-3 illustrates the steps in the differentiation of melanosomes. Originating from the free ribosomes in the cytoplasm are slender fibrils, presumably protein, that aggregate into larger and larger fibers. Melanin accumulates on these fibers, eventually obscuring the fine structure, and the fibers are then gradually enclosed within a membrane-like envelope. The mature melanosome is an electron-dense body showing no internal structure.

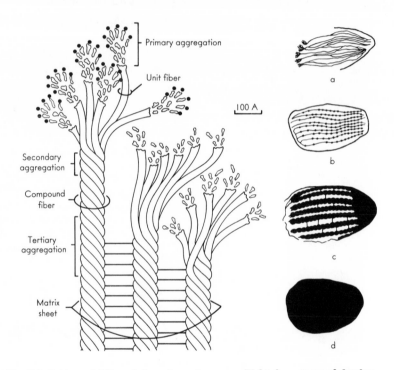

Fig. 7-3. Pattern of differentiation of a melanosome. Right, four stages of development, with fiber formation within the matrix sheet (a), and then the progressive accumulation of melanin on the fibers until the melanosome appears as a solid structure (b, c, and d). Left, detailed interpretation of the origin of the protein fibers from the ribosomes of the cytoplasm (small solid black bodies) and the grouping of six fibers into a compound fiber. (Courtesy Dr. F. Moyer.)

Many known genes influence the coloring of vertebrate animals. A study of these genes in correlation with the developing melanosome shows that they influence the number and arrangement of the fibers, the character and distribution of melanin in the melanosome, and the size, shape, and distribution of melanosomes. The system, therefore, is a beautiful example of how genes in the nucleus bring about changes within the organelles of the cytoplasm during the course of differentiation.

Differentiation vs. Growth

If we contrast differentiation with growth, we find, without knowing why, that these processes tend to be mutually exclusive. Where growth is, to varying degrees, an unending process of multiplication of similar units, differentiation is the extraction of a unit from the mass, thus making it distinctive. In the process, differentiation tends to prevent the further multiplication of the cell. Therefore, the more differentiated a cell has become, the less likely it is to divide. The cell thus becomes committed to a course of action it cannot readily change.

Let us examine a bit more closely what we mean when we say a cell is "committed." Figure 7-4 shows diagrammatically the course of development in vertebrate animals. When the cells near their final form as mature, differentiated structures, their potentiality for further change narrows as their specialization becomes more pronounced. Professor C. H. Waddington, the English embryologist, has very neatly expressed this idea of commitment by his diagram of a developmental landscape (Fig. 7-5).

Fig. 7-4. Diagrammatic representation of the pattern of progressive differentiation from unfertilized egg to mature tissues in a vertebrate. The three major tissue layers (ectoderm, mesoderm, and endoderm) originate early, and progressively give rise to the cells of the major organs. Dashed lines indicate an influence of one tissue on another during the course of development. Note that the eye has a double origin from both ectoderm and mesoderm. (Courtesy Dr. B. H. Willier.)

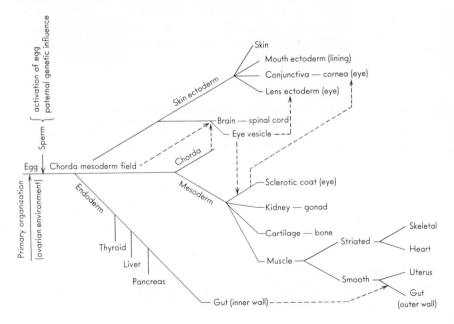

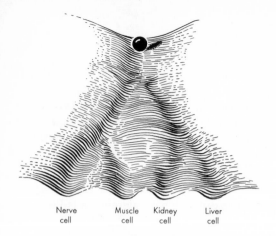

Nerve | Muscle | Kidney | Liver
cell | cell | cell | cell

Fig. 7-5. A scheme to illustrate how an uncommitted cell (represented by a ball) may become committed by rolling down one of the channels of differentiation. (After C. H. Waddington, The Strategy of the Genes. **New York:** **Macmillan, 1957.)**

He visualizes a generalized cell as a ball rolling downhill toward its final destiny, a destiny that depends on which of the many valleys the ball rolls through.

Let us express what we have been saying in more specific terms. Figure 7-6 illustrates the general course of early development in an animal such as Amphioxus. If we shake the four-celled stage apart, we find that each cell is capable of developing into a normal, if slightly smaller, organism; such development will occur even if we pinch the *blastula* in two by a hair loop. If we wait until the *gastrula* stage to disrupt development, however, only abnormal and incompletely formed individuals will result. Something obviously has been lost by the cells of the gastrula that was present in earlier ones, and the two halves of the severed embryo are no longer equivalent. Thus the destiny of some cells has already been determined by the gastrula stage even though no obvious change has taken place, and from this point on each part can only perform its "committed" role.

An embryologist has another way of approaching this problem. He cuts certain cells out of an embryo and transplants them to other embryos. If he transplants a group of young and undifferentiated cells to the future

Fig. 7-6. Early developmental stages of Amphioxus from the egg (top left) through the blastula (bottom middle) to the gastrula (bottom right) stages. Although the size of the embryo remains much the same until gastrulation (infolding), cell size and shape are being constantly altered by division and the pressure of adjoining cells. (Reprinted with permission from R. Gerard, Unresting Cells. **New York:** **Harper, 1949.)**

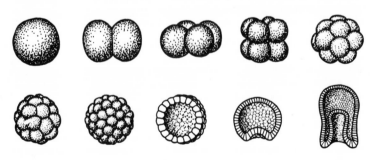

head region of another embryo, the transplanted cells become part of the head region; if he transplants them to the back, they will become part of the back musculature; if to the posterior part, they become part of the tail. But if he transplants "committed" cells from an older embryo in the same way, instead of becoming an integral part of the region to which they are transplanted, they tend rather to retain their own identity and even to modify the surrounding cells. This is well illustrated by an experiment done in the chick embryo. If the leg bud, which has no resemblance to a mature leg in any way, is removed from a young chick embryo and is transplanted to the body cavity of another embryo, the cells in the bud live, continue to increase in number, and eventually form therein a very well-developed leg with bones and muscles (Fig. 7-7). Yet the bud at the time of transplantation had no bone or muscle cells. In terms of Waddington's landscape, however, they had already entered a "valley" leading to leg formation, a valley down which they continued to roll and from which they could not escape.

Differentiation as Loss or Acquisition

Differentiation, consequently, begins long before any visible change takes place in the cells. Such changes, of course, must be preceded by chemical alterations that the cell apparently cannot undo once they have occurred. We must admit, however, that our present knowledge of these changes and the cause of their initiation is fragmentary indeed. There seems to be no doubt, on the other hand, that the differentiation of cells

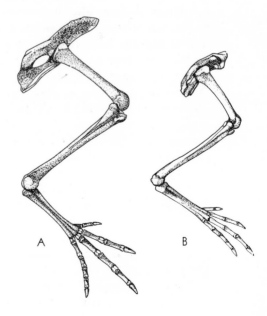

Fig. 7-7. An example of a structure that develops after transplantation in a reasonably normal fashion. (A) Normal leg bones of a chick 18 days after incubation; (B) A slightly smaller but a reasonably complete set of leg bones which developed after the hind limb bud (similar to the limb buds shown in Fig. 8-3) was transplanted to the body cavity. At the time of transplantation, the limb bud showed no evidence of bone or muscle, but the cells had already been "committed" to leg formation, a process of differentiation which continued even though the limb bud had been removed to a foreign location. (V. Hamburger and M. Waugh, Physiological Zoology, XIII, 1940, 367–380.)

can occur either through the *loss of old functions* or through the *acquisition of new ones*. We should now examine these possibilities in somewhat greater detail, for loss and acquisition may not be quite so opposite as the words imply.

A mature nerve cell traces its ancestry back to the original fertilized egg, although it is, of course, very different from the egg both in morphology and in function. Irreversible changes occur along the way, and the early versatility of the egg is sacrificed for the special property of conduction that characterizes nerves. Since if a nerve is cut, the axon can be patched up, it has evidently not lost all power of repair. On the other hand, it cannot divide to form new nerve cells. If a nerve cell dies, therefore, it cannot be replaced, but this loss in the power of division is compensated for by the acquisition of a new ability, namely, the capacity to conduct electrical impulses rapidly and efficiently.

We could, of course, assume that the original egg was capable of doing all the things that each differentiated cell can do, and that these abilities, residing in various parts of the cell, were segregated out by cell division. This possibility seems unlikely, however, when we consider that each of the cells of an early embryo can, when shaken apart, form normal individuals. A more likely supposition is that the egg contains, in the coded information in its DNA, the potentiality of all properties of all cells, and that as the differentiation of cells takes place, some potentialities are accentuated as others are suppressed or even lost. A consideration of the development of a chicken heart will make this clear.

The chicken heart begins to appear as a morphologically visible structure about 24 hours after incubation, and the first heart beats occur early in the second day. The cells that form the heart migrate from other regions into the heart-forming area, as indicated in Fig. 7-8, but what we want to know is when the heart-forming cells first become identified as potential heart cells. To find this out we determine at what stage the cells begin to form chemical substances peculiar to heart cells. These substances are proteins, and 75 per cent of heart protein consists of *actin, myosin,* and *tropomyosin,* the proteins that are necessary for muscle contraction. Heart myosin, however, is different from leg-muscle myosin and can be distinguished from it by chemical tests. Tests for actin and myosin reveal that these proteins are more generally formed by cells earlier in an embryo's life than later (Fig. 7-9), and that the myosin appears earlier and more widely spread than does actin, although both are localized later in the same region. It is possible that the localization occurs through the migration of cells, but it is more likely that some cells lose their ability to synthesize myosin, whereas others, in the heart-forming region, have this ability accentuated.

The interesting point is that we can chemically recognize heart cells long before they have either reached the heart region or have assumed a shape characteristic of heart-muscle cells. Also, if we interfere with the early synthesis of myosin by giving the cells an inhibitor, antimycin A, we can prevent the formation of the heart.

These heart studies emphasize that the differentiation of cells is essentially a change in cellular proteins. Most, if not all, of the morphological features of the cell have proteins in their chemical make-up; a change in these features is undoubtedly a reflection of a previous alteration in the proteins. A change in metabolic function must also involve a protein change, because all reactions in the cell are governed by enzymes which themselves are proteins. Since the nuclei of most somatic cells appear to be similar, we must therefore assume that most cellular alterations occurring during differentiation take place in the cytoplasm. As a further corollary, since particular strains of cells can increase and perpetuate their kind, the cytoplasm as well as the nucleus must be endowed with the capacity for self-perpetuation. We do not yet know what this means in chemical terms.

Fig. 7-8. The heart-forming areas of the chick embryo from which cells can migrate into the site where actual formation takes place. The cells move first toward the tail and then through the region of the primitive streak (stippled area) into the mesoderm (middle layer of cells), after which they assemble in the head area on either side of the primitive streak. The intensity of the cross-hatching is a measure of the number of cells coming from a given area. (Courtesy Dr. Mary E. Rawles.)

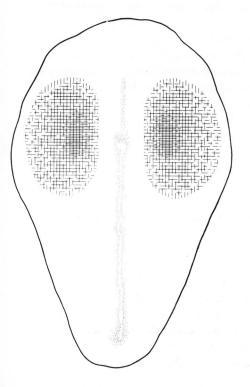

Nuclear Differentiation

The nucleus itself can undergo a degree of differentiation. The nucleus has a set of genes containing coded information in its DNA that exercises control over the cell and directs its destiny. But is the nucleus of a liver cell the same as that of a nerve cell? Are all genes active at all times? The answer is probably "no" in both instances, even though the critical information is difficult to obtain. But certain experiments suggest a solution. For example, with very fine pipettes it is possible to take a nucleus from a cell of the blastula and put it into an egg that has had its own nucleus removed. Such an egg will withstand this puncturing and develop normally. However, if a nucleus is taken from a later embryo after the gastrula stage and transplanted similarly to an enucleated egg, then de-

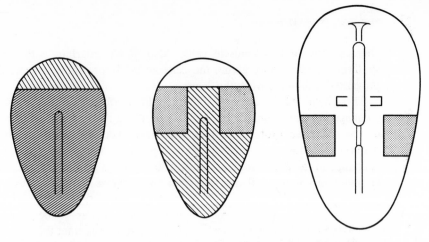

Fig. 7-9. The distribution of heart-muscle proteins in three stages of the chick embryo. Heart actin (dotted area) is formed later than heart myosin (cross-hatched area) and in a much more restricted area of the embryo, but myosin formation itself becomes more restricted as the embryo develops. The density of cross-hatching indicates the intensity of myosin formation. (Courtesy Dr. J. Ebert.)

velopment is abnormal and only partial. The nuclei from differentiated, or "committed," cells are restricted in their developmental control, and they lack the versatility of the nuclei of undifferentiated cells. We do not yet know how this restriction of power arises, but it does suggest that the differentiation of cells can be both cytoplasmic and nuclear.

We also know that chromosomes often exhibit morphological differentiation. In the larvae of flies such as *Drosophila melanogaster,* the cells of the salivary glands contain very large, banded chromosomes, as shown in Fig. 7-10. They arise by the growth and elongation of ordinary chromosomes, and their appearance in tissues other than that of the salivary gland may also change during development. Whether the changes, which affect the appearance of particular bands in the chromosomes, indicate that the genes in these areas are particularly active at one stage but not at another is a possibility that needs further exploration.

INTEGRATION

We can now appreciate that the fertilized egg is a rather remarkable cell. It is primarily an organism in its simplest, or undeveloped, state; it is a cell only secondarily, and differs from other cells in its potentiality for total development. Growth and differentiation, as we have seen, are two of the processes by which development is achieved. When we consider development in terms of cells, therefore, we find a progression from initially simple and uniform cell types to complex and diverse ones; the plastic, versatile cell becomes stabilized with an unalterable structure; cells with general functions develop highly specialized functions.

But growth, relative growth rates, and differentiation are not enough

Fig. 7-10. Salivary-gland chromosomes of Drosphilia melanogaster. Top, a smear preparation from the salivary gland of a female, showing the X-chromosome, the arms of the two autosomes (2L, 2R, 3L, and 3R), and the small 4-chromosome. The diploid number of chromosomes is present, but the homologues are in intimate synapsis, and are united by their centric heterochromatin into a chromocenter. Middle, enlarged drawing of the 4-chromosome showing the banded structure; the diffuse chromocenter is at the left, and the two homologues are intimately paired. Bottom, metaphase chromosomes from a ganglion cell, with an arrow pointing to the 4-chromosomes, and with a scale to indicate differences in size between the two types of chromosomes. (Top, courtesy Dr. B. P. Kaufmann; middle and bottom, C. B. Bridges, Journal of Heredity, 26, 1935, 60–64.)

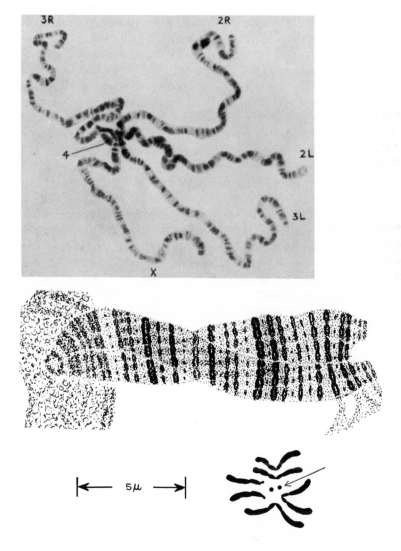

to account for all of development. The whole course of development of an organism, from the moment of fertilization to death, is characterized by a *unity* and a *harmony* of structure and behavior that cannot be explained by these processes. The egg, the seed, the embryo, and the larva are all organisms as complete as is the mature individual that arises from them. Although their development may not be fully realized, at all times they behave like, and indeed are, fully functional living entities, and they develop as a *whole,* not simply as a collection of cells or a group of cells.

This phenomenon of unity we call *integration,* but we must admit that it is difficult to define and even more difficult to comprehend. To understand integration we must have an intimate knowledge of organization at the molecular, cellular, tissue, and organ levels, and this we do not possess except in a fragmentary way. We do know that integration depends on a number of factors: chemical stimuli such as hormones, cell movements such as those involved in the formation of the gonads and in the infolding that produces the gastrula; cell interactions such as those responsible for the formation of a compound structure such as the eye (Fig. 7-4); and the processes of differentiation that impress upon an undeveloped limb bud the ability to form a complete leg even after the bud is removed from its normal position of development (Fig. 7-7).

We can highlight the significance of integration by posing several questions that we cannot yet answer. Why do animals reach a mature size and stop growing? What determines the life span of organisms? What determines the size relationship between one part of the body and another? What is it that determines *morphogenesis,* the origin and realization of form? How does one phase of development affect succeeeding phases? We must answer these and many other questions before we begin to understand development as an over-all process of life. Some of the aspects of development can possibly be approached and explained at the cellular level, but others, such as morphogenesis, seem to involve a higher order of organization in which the individual cell plays a subordinate role. And at a vital, practical level, our ability to control cancer, which results from the growth and escape of cells from regulative control, rests on our comprehending development as a rigidly governed system of chemical checks and balances.

The Cell in Death

Any individual has a life span that is characteristic of the species to which it belongs. In some instances, the life span is rather sharply limited: 17 years for certain periodic locusts. Usually, however, we think of the life span as an average figure: a few days for certain insects, a few months for annual plants, three score and 10 years for man, 250 to 300 years for an oak tree. The sequoia of our West Coast and the bristle-cone pine of California's White Mountains are probably the longest-lived organisms; some of the trees reach an age of several thousand years.

Cells, too, have a life span which they complete and then pass out of existence. And like organisms, cell strains, even in the same organism, have characteristic long or short life spans. Yet it is entirely reasonable to consider some cells to be immortal. When a unicellular organism divides, the life of the single cell becomes part of the life of two new cells, and as long as the species lives so does the cell; the life of a member of such a species, then, stretches in an unbroken chain back to some original cell in the past. Among sexually reproducing organisms, only the cells of the germ line can lay claim to immortality, for they are the only cells that span the generations and keep the species alive. But among the cells of the body, death is a necessary process because if its role is altered the functioning of the organism will be affected drastically. As a biological problem, and apart from the death of an organism, there are two broad categories of cellular death: (1) that resulting from the wear and tear of existence, which must be counterbalanced by an equivalent amount of cell replacement, and (2) that resulting from the normal process of development.

CELL REPLACEMENT

It has been estimated that a human being has a new body every seven years, the time it takes for the old cells of the body to be replaced by new ones. Even if accurate, this figure is very misleading, for some parts of the body require a constant replacement of cells while other parts are incapable of replacement. By the time of birth, all the nerve and muscle cells of the body have been formed, and they will continue to function as long as the individual lives (barring injury). If a nerve cell is destroyed, it is not replaced by another; the nerve cell cannot divide once it is fully differentiated, and no nerve-cell replacement center exists. It was long thought that this was also true for muscle cells, but recent studies suggest that the muscles are capable of limited replacement. That an organ remains constant in size, however, is not indicative of its rate of replacement; unless the cellular conditions are known, the constancy of size merely indicates that there is no net gain or loss of cells. The death of the old cells is equalled by the production of new cells.

Some biologists estimate that the human body loses 1 to 2 per cent of its cells through death each day. Body weight, therefore, would double every 50 to 100 days if no cells died, and if cell division proceeded normally. If the weight of the body remains constant, therefore, these dead cells must be replaced by new ones, by billions of cells every day. Since none of these is produced in the muscles or the nervous tissue, there must be some active centers of death and replacement elsewhere. And there are, in, for instance, the protective layers, and in the blood, digestive, and reproductive systems. The other organs of the body have much slower replacement rates; a liver cell, for example, has an average life span of about 18 months. Consequently, if we look at a liver slice under a microscope, we expect to find very few cells in division. On the other hand, if a portion of the human liver is lost, the rate of cell replacement is stepped up until the original size is once more approximated.

The outer surface of the human body is covered with a protective layer, which is mostly skin, but which also includes the lining of all openings, the cornea of the eye, and such modified skin derivatives as nails and hair. The cells of these structures are constantly being lost through death: The skin sloughs off, and the growing nails and hair are composed of dead cells. The process of replacement, then, must be a relatively rapid one. The underlying cells are constantly dividing, and are pushed outward toward the skin surface, while the outermost cells become *cornified* (hardened) as they die (Fig. 8-1). It takes approximately 12 to 14 days for a cell in the skin of the forearm to move from the dividing to the outermost layer of the skin. Callouses on the hands are thickened areas of dead cells, and a needle can be pushed through these areas without causing pain or drawing blood.

The cornea of the eye is a special type of skin in which the rate of cell death and replacement is high. The cornea, in fact, is an excellent type of tissue to examine for active cell division. Since it is only a few cell-layers thick, it can be stripped off (the salamander and rat are good animals to use for this purpose), fixed, stained, and mounted intact on a microscope slide. The dying cells can be seen at the outer surface, while the underneath cells are in active division.

The cells of the blood are not formed in the blood. The red blood cells are derived from the bone marrow, and the white cells (*leucocytes*) from the lymph nodes, spleen, and thymus gland. Together, these cells and the *plasma* constitute the blood, which has an average ratio of one white cell to 400–500 red cells. The blood-forming areas usually manage to maintain the cell ratios, but obviously there must be a high loss of cells to offset the new ones formed

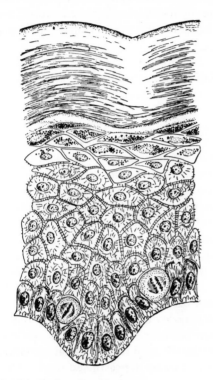

Fig. 8-1. Section through human skin showing the progression of cells from the region of division at the base up to the horny layer of dead cells at the surface. The surface layer is continuously eroded away, but is being as continuously replaced by cells moving into place from below.

or the blood system would clog up. Since each type of cell dies off at a relatively constant rate, we need consider here only one, the red blood cells. Their life span is about 120 days. They lack a nucleus, losing it as they pass into the blood stream, so the wear of passage through the vessels cannot be repaired, and they grow fragile and finally burst. Certain types of illness may shorten their life span. In a patient with pernicious anemia, the life span is reduced to about 85 days; with sickle-cell anemia, to 42 days. The rate of replacement cannot keep up with the loss of cells, and the red-cell count falls below normal and results in an anemic state. The cause of the shortened life span is not known.

The digestive system is another organ with a cell death rate that is very high. Figures for human beings are not known, but it has been estimated that the cells lining the intestine of the rat are replaced every 38 hours.

In the plant kingdom, we find that the lower plants—the algae and fungi, in particular—have a rather low loss of cells through death. In the higher plants, however, the rate is enormous. In herbaceous plants, all the cells above ground are lost every season. But consider a large tree. The annual loss of cells in the leaves, flowers, and fruits (only the seeds remain alive) is high enough, but when you add all the cells going to form dead wood and bark, you can see that the loss of cells through death in animals is small by comparison. Yet a high rate of cell death is as much a pattern of existence as the continuation of living cells.

The difference between higher plants and animals, as regards longevity and cell replacement, is even more profound than it appears at first glance. A plant such as a tree preserves its "youthfulness" and vigor in two ways. First by continuing the processes of cell division and differentiation indefinitely. And second by paralleling these processes with an equally continuous succession of cell deaths, either by discarding the cells as in the case of leaves or by converting them into dead supportive tissue as in the case of wood. The younger the living cells the less "aged" is the tree. A mammal, on the other hand, achieves its longevity by an exactly opposite process, that is, by preserving the majority of its cells in a living, functioning state. As was pointed out earlier, however, a cell that does not divide is destined to die; the result is that the life span of a mammal, or indeed any vertebrate, is short compared to that of the longest-lived trees.

CELL DEATH AND NORMAL DEVELOPMENT

When we think of normal development, we naturally think of an increase in the number of cells, their subsequent differentiation into specialized cells, and the grouping of these cells into organs and organ systems. This process is dynamic and creative, so you may consider it incongruous to characterize cell death as a vital and necessary aspect of development. Cell death, however, plays two very significant roles in development. The first of these, *metamorphosis,* has long been known; the second, the role of cell death in the shaping of organs and body contours, is only beginning to be appreciated as a phase of development.

Metamorphosis involves a change in shape (the transformation of a larval form of an organism into an adult) and a change in organs when one mode of life is exchanged for another. Two well-known examples are the metamorphosis of a tadpole into an adult frog, and of a caterpillar into a pupa and then into a butterfly or a moth.

A tadpole is transformed into a frog without an appreciable change in size, and in the common American leopard frog the process takes about a year. The tadpole that emerges from the egg, and the large tadpole about to metamorphose have the same general shape; in its conversion into a frog, it grows legs and loses its tail, which is devoured by wandering cells, or *phagocytes,* that are carried by the blood stream to the tail region where they gradually consume the muscles, nerves, skin, and other tissues. The skin shrinks and eventually the tail is reduced to a mere stump. In addition, the tissues in the digestive and excretory systems are extensively reorganized. We can speed up or slow down the process experimentally, for in the frog, metamorphosis is, at least in part, under the control of an iodine-containing hormone from the *thyroid gland.* More thyroid hormone accelerates the process, less reduces its speed and may even prolong larval life and shape indefinitely.

The character of metamorphosis in insects varies quite widely, and cell death is not always a major aspect of change. In the simplest type of metamorphosis, the cells of a particular larval tissue are retained to form the corresponding tissue in the adult, and only minor differences in growth and differentiation are needed to bring this about. In these cases of *incomplete metamorphosis,* the form of the insect is only slightly altered as the larva matures to adult proportions. Good examples of this type of metamorphosis are found in locusts, grasshoppers and cockroaches.

In *complete metamorphosis,* the larval and adult forms are totally different from each other. The larva, or caterpillar, is converted into a pupa, the larval skin hardens and shrinks into the outer skin, or *puparium,* of the pupa, and the larval tissues are almost completely destroyed. The adult develops during pupation, and adult tissues arise from *imaginal buds* that form in the larva and that escape cell death. These buds can be regarded as zones of persistent embryonic tissue in which the potentiality for growth and differentiation is suppressed during larval life, and is only realized when the *juvenile hormone,* which controls larval growth, lessens its normal activity and the hormone concerned with metamorphosis becomes fully effective.

Figure 8-2 shows the location of certain imaginal buds of the larva of the fruit fly, *Drosophila.* Much of the brain and nervous system will survive cell destruction, but the intestine, blood system, muscles, and skin will be totally destroyed.

The last type of cell death we shall consider is that involved in the shaping of organs. Form can be achieved by relative rates of cell death as well as by relative rates of cell growth. As organs develop during morphogenesis, for instance, excess cells are often a hindrance, and these

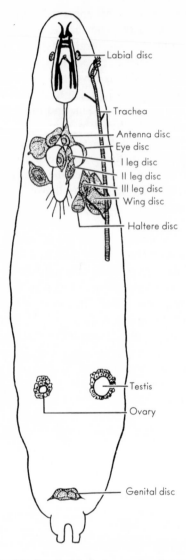

Labial disc

Trachea

Antenna disc
Eye disc
I leg disc
II leg disc
III leg disc
Wing disc

Haltere disc

Testis

Ovary

Genital disc

Fig. 8-2. Imaginal buds in a mature larva of Drosophila. During metamorphosis most of the larval structures except the nervous system will undergo destruction, while the adult tissues will arise from the imaginal buds, some of which are indicated. The buds form during larval life, but do not undergo differentiation until the influence of the larval hormones wanes. (Reprinted with permission by D. Bodenstein from Biology of Drosophila. M. Demerec, New York: Wiley, 1950.)

transient cells that are of use to the embryo or larva but not to the adult must be removed (the tail of the tadpole is a case in point). Or when an organism forms secretory ducts, cells die instead of pulling apart to provide for the central hole, or lumen. Many organs form by the infolding of tissues that then fuse along their edges—for example, the eye and part of the nervous system—and the seams where fusion takes place are removed by cell death. Fingers and toes are separated from one another in the same way; if the separation is incomplete, a webbed condition results.

One of the most arresting instances of cell death as a morphogenetic phenomenon is the one that frees the elbow of the wing of the chick from the body wall and gives the wing its characteristic shape. Figure 8-3 illustrates the region in question. These cells die as a line of cellular destruction moves from the body area along the front and back of the wing toward its tip, thus separating the elbow region from the body wall. What is most fascinating of all in this process, however, is that when these cells are removed and transplanted to another part of the embryo, the cells *die on sched-*

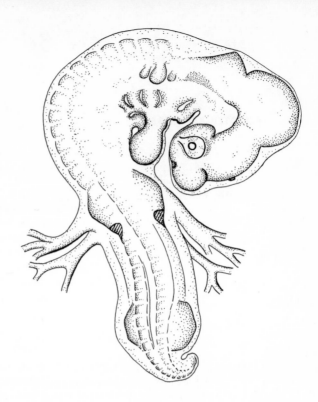

Fig. 8-3. Diagram of a chick embryo 72 hours after incubation. The wing buds are beginning to form below the head region, and it is the cells in the cross-hatched areas that will die in order to cut out the "elbow" region.

ule (at approximately 4 days of age) as if they were still in their original site. Their time of death had already been determined by some unknown change that had taken place within them, and once embarked on their course of destruction they could not escape. If we can, in the future, understand the mechanism responsible for this phenomenon, we may well be on our way to comprehending the larger problem of aging and of fixed life spans.

SELECTED READINGS

Bourne, G. H., *Division of Labor in Cells*. New York: Academic Press, 1962. A paperback volume containing much recent information on the fine structures of cells.

Butler, J. A. V., *Inside the Living Cell*. New York: Basic Books, 1959. A nontechnical account of cell structure and function and of the reactions of cells to radiations, chemicals, cancer, and aging.

Darlington, C. D., *Chromosome Botany*. London: Allen & Unwin, 1956. An account of nuclear cytology as it relates to the evolution of plant species.

Gerard, R. W., *Unresting Cells*. New York: Harper, 1940. One of the finest books available on cells; should be read by every student of biology.

Greeson, R. A. R., *Essentials of General Cytology*. Edinburgh: University Press, 1948. A sound general account of both nuclear and cytoplasmic cytology.

Hoffman, J. G., *The Life and Death of Cells*. New York: Hanover, 1957. A semipopular account of the microscopic realm of cells, as viewed through modern theories of matter and energy.

Hughes, A., *A History of Cytology*. New York: Abelard-Schuman, 1959. An excellent historical account of microscopical observations, the cell theory, cell division, theories of inheritance, studies of the cytoplasm, and the place of cellular theory in general biology.

McLeish, J., and B. Snoad, *Looking at Chromosomes*. New York: St. Martin's Press, 1958. A small book describing mitotic and meiotic divisions in the lily, and illustrated by a superb collection of photographs.

Bloom, W., and D. W. Fawcett, *A Textbook of Histology*. Philadelphia: Saunders, 1962. Widely used by medical students, this is one of the best American texts available in its field; beautifully illustrated in color and in black and white, and with many electron micrographs.

Strehler, B. L., *Time, Cells, and Aging*. New York: Academic Press, 1962. An excellent small volume dealing with aging as a cellular problem.

Swanson, C. P., *Cytology and Cytogenetics*. Englewood Cliffs, N. J.: Prentice-Hall, 1957. A detailed account of chromosomal structure and behavior, particularly as these relate to genetics and evolution.

Wilson, E. B., *The Cell in Development and Heredity*. New York: Macmillan, 1925. A classic of biological literature, with discussions oriented toward embryology; worthwhile for both beginner and expert.

Index

118